The American Journey

Unit 10 Resources
Turning Points

Glencoe
McGraw-Hill

New York, New York   Columbus, Ohio   Chicago, Illinois   Peoria, Illinois   Woodland Hills, California

BOOK ORGANIZATION

Glencoe offers resources that accompany *The American Journey* to expand, enrich, review, and assess every lesson you teach and for every student you teach. Now Glencoe has organized its many resources for the way you teach.

How This Book is Organized

Each unit resources book offers blackline masters at unit, chapter, and section levels for each unit. Each book is divided into three parts—unit-based resources, chapter-based resources and section-based resources. Glencoe has included tabs at the side of every activity page in this book to help you navigate through it.

Unit-Based Resources

We have organized this book so that all resources appear in the first part of the unit resources books. Although you may choose to use the specific activities at any time during the course of unit study, Glencoe has placed these resources up front so that you can review your options. For example, although American Literature Reading 1 appears in the front part of this book, you may plan to use this activity in class during the study of Native Americans in Chapter 11.

Chapter-Based and Section-Based Resources

Chapter-based resources follow the unit materials. For example, Chapter 1 blackline masters appear in this book immediately following Unit 1 materials. The materials appear in the order you teach—Chapter 1 activities; Chapter 1, Section 1 activities; Chapter 1, Section 2 activities; and so on. Following the end of the last section activity for Chapter 1, the Chapter 2 resources appear.

A Complete Answer Key

A complete answer key appears at the back of this book. This answer key includes answers for every activity in the book in the order in which the activities appear.

Glencoe/McGraw-Hill

A Division of *The McGraw-Hill Companies*

Copyright © by The McGraw-Hill Companies, Inc. All rights reserved. Permission is granted to reproduce the material contained herein on the condition that such material be reproduced only for classroom use; be provided to students, teachers, and families without charge; and be used solely in conjunction with *The American Journey*. Any other reproduction, for use or sale, is prohibited without written permission from the publisher.

Send all inquiries to:
Glencoe/McGraw-Hill
8787 Orion Place
Columbus, OH 43240

ISBN 0-07-825219-9

Printed in the United States of America

1 2 3 4 5 6 7 8 9 10 024 08 07 06 05 04 03 02

TABLE OF CONTENTS

To The Teacher

The Total Package—*The American Journey* Unit Resources

Glencoe's Unit Resource books are packed with activities for the varied needs of all of your students. They include the following activities.

Activities Found in Unit Resources Booklets

- **Citizenship Activities: History and Your Community**
  These activities are designed to provide students with a variety of opportunities to participate in their communities at the grassroots level. These service-learning projects help students understand how history affects their own lives on a daily basis.

- **Economics and History Activities**
  These activities are designed to provide students with the opportunity to analyze and interpret historical concepts and events in relation to economics. These assignments make extensive use of maps, graphic organizers, and economic data to help students appreciate how history and economics are interrelated.

- **Cooperative Learning Activities**
  These activities offer students management directions for working together on a variety of activities that enrich prior learning. These activities promote a shared learning experience as well as encourage individual accountability among group members.

- **American Literature Readings**
  These readings provide students with the opportunity to read literature by or about people who lived during different historical periods. Each selection is preceded by background information and a guided reading suggestion, and followed by comprehension and critical thinking questions.

- **Interdisciplinary Connections**
  These activities intersect history with other areas of study, such as art, geography, math, and economics. These activities give students a well-rounded picture of the correlation between history and other subjects.

- **Hands-On History Activities**
  These practical activities give students the chance to do as their forebears did by making utensils and foods commonly used in early history. Each activity gives the student little-known facts and insights about that particular historical period.

- **History Simulations and Problem Solving**
  These activities provide situations for students to use critical thinking and other American history skills in simulated historical settings. These reenactment activities give students the experience of participating in the democratic process through debates, mock trials, voting, and political campaigns.

- **Vocabulary Activities**
  These review and reinforcement activities help students to master unfamiliar terms used in the student text. The worksheets emphasize identification of word meanings and provide visual and kinesthetic reinforcement of language skills.

- **Chapter Skills Activities**
  These activities allow students to practice their critical thinking and social studies skills with the information learned in the student text and apply it to real world situations. These chapter-based activities will help students develop the basic skills needed to adapt to new situations and content.

- **Critical Thinking Skills Activities**
  These activities help students develop their ability to interpret, compare, contrast, and assess information and use it to analyze, make predictions, and reach logical and valid judgements and conclusions. These high level thinking activities are vitally important to a student's ability to function in an ever-changing world.

- **Geography and History Activities**
  These activities help students become familiar with map skills and the role geography plays in history. Students will interpret and analyze maps in relation to historical events.

- **Time Line Activities**
  Time lines are used to help students become aware of chronology in major historical events. Comparative time lines allow students to see relationships among events in different regions of the country, among events in different countries, or among events on different continents.

- **Linking Past and Present Activities**
  By recognizing the link between the past and the present, students will better understand the relevancy of history to their lives. For example, exploring the changes in information technology from the printing press to computerized desktop publishing will help students realize the past is a prologue to what is present in today's world.

- **Primary Resource Readings**
  This booklet allows students to see history through the eyes of those who witnessed historic events, lived in historic periods, and participated in historic cultures. Each reading is preceded by an interpretive paragraph and concludes with an engaging activity related to the primary resource reading.

- **Guided Reading Activities**
  These activities provide help for students who are having difficulty organizing the information found in the sections. Students fill in missing information in outlines and sentence completion activities and respond to short-answer questions.

- **Reteaching Activities**
  These are a variety of activities designed to enable students to visualize the connections among facts in their textbook and major review concepts. Graphs, charts, and tables are among the many types of graphic organizers used.

- **Enrichment Activities**
  These activities introduce students to content that is different from, but related to, the themes, ideas, and information in the student textbook. Enrichment activities help students develop a broader and deeper understanding of the concepts and ideas presented in the sections.

Unit 10 Resources

UNIT 10

Citizenship Activity 10

UNIT 10

Civil Rights and Your Community

WHY IT'S IMPORTANT

What are civil rights? How are your civil rights guaranteed? Why is it important for you to know your civil rights?

BACKGROUND

On August 9, 1960, ten African Americans sat down at a lunch counter in the S.H. Kress store in Greenville, South Carolina, and asked to be served lunch. The manager of the store called the police, turned off the lights, and announced that the lunch counter and store were closed. Everyone was asked to leave. The ten African Americans quietly remained at the lunch counter.

When the police arrived, they arrested all ten individuals and took them to the local police station. The manager acknowledged that the ten African Americans were cooperative; however, a city ordinance did not allow them to be served at the lunch counter. At the time, African Americans were not allowed to eat at the lunch counters because the lunch counters were reserved for white customers only. These types of laws were meant to keep African Americans separate from the white population, and African Americans saw this as unjust.

Because of these types of laws, each of the ten African Americans was ordered to pay a $100 trespassing fine or spend 30 days in jail. The state court upheld this decision. The United States Supreme Court reversed the state court decision, declaring that the city ordinance under which the store manager had acted promoted discrimination and, therefore, violated the civil rights of the ten individuals.

Civil rights are the rights guaranteed to all individuals by the United States Constitution and by other laws. Laws protecting civil rights guarantee that every individual has equal protection under the law and that there cannot be any discrimination.

Study the table below and then answer the questions that follow.

CIVIL RIGHTS LEGISLATION

Year	Legislation	Description
1865	Thirteenth Amendment	Banned slavery and involuntary servitude
1868	Fourteenth Amendment	Granted citizenship to all persons born or naturalized in the United States
1870	Fifth Amendment	Banned voting discrimination based on race, color, or previous condition of being a slave
1875	Civil Rights Act of 1875	Gave all citizens the right to make contracts, buy property, and testify in court
1920	Nineteenth Amendment	Granted women the right to vote
1924	Snyder Act	Granted citizenship to Native Americans
1964	Twenty-fourth Amendment	Barred the use of poll taxes, which were fees that a voter had to pay in order to vote, in federal elections
1964	Civil Rights Act of 1964	Made discrimination illegal; ordered restaurants and other businesses to serve all people without regard to race, color, religion, or national origin
1965	Voting Rights Act of 1965	Gave the federal government the power to force local officials to allow African Americans to register to vote
1972	Equal Opportunity Employment Act	Banned discrimination on the basis of race, color, religion, or national origin in employment
1990	Americans with Disabilities Act	Provided people with disabilities equal access to housing, employment, education, and public buildings

1

(continued)

Citizenship Activity 10

QUESTIONS TO ASK

1. How are the civil rights of individuals protected?

_____

2. Which amendments to the Constitution protect voting rights?

_____

3. Which amendments have affected you or your family? How have they affected you?

_____

_____

4. What are two examples of changes made to a public place, such as a restaurant or a bus, which are results of the Americans with Disabilities Act?

_____

_____

YOUR TASK

Find out more about how civil rights laws have impacted your community. For example, have property laws changed, allowing people of all races to buy homes or open businesses, or have jobs always been open to all races and people with disabilities?

HOW TO DO IT

Interview a real-estate agent, a business owner, or a public official such as a local librarian, clerk, or police officer. Ask how civil rights laws affect the people in your community. For example, you could ask a business owner about how civil rights laws influence who he or she employs. Write a one-page report on what you learned.

FOLLOW-UP ACTIVITY

As a class, discuss how civil rights laws affect your daily life. Talk about where you live and who your neighbors and classmates are. Remember that as recent as the 1960s, your classmates would be of all one race, as schools were segregated. Decorate your bulletin board with pictures and articles that demonstrate the effects of civil rights laws. Show women, African Americans, or Native Americans holding local offices, or take pictures of local business owners of different races and get quotes about their experiences with civil rights.

> **DID YOU KNOW?**
> Jackie Robinson was the first African American to break the race barrier in professional baseball. Jackie Robinson signed with the Brooklyn Dodgers in 1945 and was a star player throughout his career. By 1949 other African Americans began playing in the major leagues.

Economics and History Activity 10

Consumer Power

BACKGROUND

After World War II, Americans enjoyed prosperity and economic growth. Men returning home from war went back into the workforce. With the booming economy, Americans were getting married and having children. The birthrate sharply increased after the war through 1961, and the number of families with three or four children increased dramatically. This increased rise in birthrate is known as the baby boom. Many of these growing families moved out of cities and into suburbs. A family car and a home were signs of success. Americans bought new products such as dishwashers and washing machines to ease their workload and allow more time for recreation. *The Ed Sullivan Show, Roy Rogers,* and *Ozzie and Harriet* were popular television programs, Hollywood turned out stars like Marilyn Monroe, and rock 'n' roll was born.

BUYING POWER

While life seemed good in the suburbs, times were not so easy in the cities and on farms. The flight of people from the cities to the suburbs left cities short on tax dollars to maintain services. Meanwhile, farm incomes were not increasing at the same rate as the incomes of city and suburban populations. Farm prices, or the price paid to the farmer for farm products, increased at a much slower rate than the personal incomes of people living in cities and suburbs. So while the buying power of people in the cities and suburbs increased, the buying power of many farm families remained about the same or decreased throughout the years.

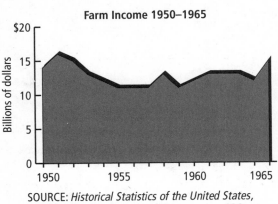

Farm Income 1950–1965

SOURCE: *Historical Statistics of the United States,* United States Department of Commerce, p. 236.

Retail Price Comparisons of Four Farm Products 1950–1965

Potatoes   Chuck roast
Pork chops   Butter

SOURCE: *Historical Statistics of the United States,* United States Department of Commerce, p. 213.

DIRECTIONS: Use the graphs to answer the following questions.

1. What was the general trend in farm income between 1950 and 1965?

_____

(continued)

Economics and History Activity 10

2. What price did chuck roast bring in 1955? How did the price of chuck roast change by 1960?

_____

_____

3. How did the price of butter change between 1950 and 1965?

_____

_____

4. What might the graph of farm income tell about life on a farm during the 1950s and 1960s?

_____

_____

CRITICAL THINKING

Making Comparisons Compare the information on the two graphs—farm income and retail prices. What changes might you expect in the United States based on the information presented in the graphs?

_____

_____

_____

_____

_____

_____

_____

_____

_____

_____

_____

★ Cooperative Learning Activity 10 ★

UNIT 10

Speaking on Vietnam

✪ BACKGROUND

Like the Civil War and the Revolutionary War, the war in Vietnam tore families apart and divided friends. Some people believed they best served their country by fighting in the war. Others believed the best way to serve the country was to refuse to serve in a war they could not support.

✪ GROUP DIRECTIONS

1. Many people alive today took part on one side or the other of the controversy surrounding the Vietnam War. Invite one or two of them to speak to the class and participate in a class discussion. If possible, invite one Vietnam veteran and one person who protested the war.

2. Identify the resources in your area for finding Vietnam veterans and people who protested the war who are willing to speak about their experiences. Ask parents, friends, and your teacher if they know of someone who might speak to your class. Talk to the Veterans of Foreign Wars and ask them to recommend a speaker.

3. Make a list of people who are available and decide who to invite to speak.

4. Work with your teacher and your guest(s) to organize the visit.

Planning for Outside Speakers

Coordinate with the speakers

- Issue invitations to the speakers and arrange dates and times.

- Assign a student to meet the speakers and make sure they know where to go. Make sure speakers have everything they need for their presentations.

- After the visit, send thank-you notes to the speakers.

Coordinate with school authorities

- Agree with your teacher on dates and times for the speakers.

- Find out school procedures for outside visitors and make sure these procedures are followed.

Coordinate the event

- Act as the moderator: introduce the speaker in the beginning, moderate the class discussion, and thank the speaker at the end.

✪ Cooperative Group Process

1. Assign group members resources to check to find possible people to speak to the class.

2. Visit, phone, write letters to, or contact via e-mail local resources to get information on possible speakers.

★ Cooperative Learning Activity 10 ★

UNIT 10

3. Meet together as a group and have each individual report on what he or she has found. Use the information to choose which speaker(s) to invite. Rank the speakers in order of preference; if your first choice cannot visit your class, you have additional speakers to contact.

4. Use the material in the box as a guide as you assign group members all the tasks involved in having an outside speaker talk to the class. Have one group member act as the overall coordinator who is responsible for making sure that all individual tasks are accomplished.

5. Research and read about the war in Vietnam. Prepare pertinent, or related, questions to ask your chosen speaker.

✪ Group Process Questions

- What is the most interesting thing you learned about the war in Vietnam?
- Which part of this project gave you the most difficulties?
- How was it helpful for you to work together?

Quick ¡CHECK✔

1. Was the goal of the assignment clear at all times? _____
_____
_____

2. Did you have trouble agreeing on who to invite to speak? _____
_____
_____

3. Were you pleased with your contribution to the project? _____
_____
_____

American Literature Reading 10

An Unpopular War

> ◪ **About the Selection** Many Americans opposed American involvement in
> Vietnam. Antiwar protesters used many means to show their opposition to the
> war, including burning their draft cards or fleeing to Canada to avoid the draft.
> The following selection, from *The Woman Warrior: Memoirs of a Girlhood
> Among Ghosts* by Maxine Hong Kingston, reveals one Chinese American
> woman's feelings about her son's participation in the war.

UNIT 10

GUIDED READING As you read, observe the details that trigger Brave Orchid's
thoughts.

from *The Woman Warrior: Memoirs of a Girlhood Among Ghosts*
by Maxine Hong Kingston

When she was about sixty-eight years old,
Brave Orchid took a day off to wait at San
Francisco International Airport for the
plane that was bringing her
sister to the United
States. She had not seen
Moon Orchid for thirty
years. She had begun
this waiting at home, getting
up a half-hour before Moon
Orchid's plane took off in
Hong Kong. Brave Orchid would add her will
power to the forces that keep an airplane up. Her
head hurt with the concentration. The plane had to be light, so no matter
how tired she felt, she dared not rest her spirit on a wing but continuously
and gently pushed up on the plane's belly. She had already been waiting at
the airport for nine hours. She was wakeful. . . .

"Are you all right, Aunt?" asked her niece.

"No, this chair hurts me. Help me pull some chairs together so I can put
my feet up." . . .

Many soldiers and sailors sat about, oddly calm, like little boys in cowboy
uniforms. (She thought "cowboy" was what you would call a Boy Scout.)
They should have been crying hysterically on their way to Vietnam. "If I see
one that looks Chinese," she thought, "I'll go over and give him some advice."
She sat up suddenly; she had forgotten about her own son, who was even
now in Vietnam. Carefully she split her attention, beaming half of it to
the ocean, into the water to keep him afloat. He was on a ship. He was in

(continued)

American Literature Reading 10

Vietnamese waters. She was sure of it. He and the other children were lying to her. They had said he was in Japan, and then they said he was in the Philippines. But when she sent him her help, she could feel that he was on a ship in Da Nang. Also she had seen the children hide the envelopes that his letters came in.

"Do you think my son is in Vietnam?" she asked her niece, who was dutifully eating.

"No. Didn't your children say he was in the Philippines?"

"Have you ever seen any of his letters with Philippine stamps on them?"

"Oh, yes. Your children showed me one."

"I wouldn't put it past them to send the letters to some Filipino they know. He puts Manila postmarks on them to fool me."

"Yes, I can imagine them doing that. But don't worry. Your son can take care of himself. All your children can take care of themselves."

"Not him. He's not like other people. Not normal at all. He sticks erasers in his ears, and the erasers are still attached to the pencil stubs. The captain will say, 'Abandon ship,' or 'Watch out for bombs,' and he won't hear. He doesn't listen to orders. I told him to flee to Canada, but he wouldn't go."

She closed her eyes. After a short while, plane and ship under control, she looked again at the children in uniforms. Some of the blond ones looked like baby chicks, their crew cuts like the downy yellow on baby chicks. You had to feel sorry for them even though they were Army and Navy Ghosts.

Suddenly her son and daughter came running. "Come, Mother. The plane's landed early. She's here already." . . .

"It's a good thing I made you come early," she said.

SOURCE: From *The Woman Warrior* by Maxine Hong Kingston. Copyright © 1976 by Maxine Hong Kingston. Reprinted by permission of Alfred A. Knopf, Inc.

DIRECTIONS: Recalling Facts Answer the following questions on a separate sheet of paper.

1. How long has it been since Brave Orchid saw her sister?

2. Why does Brave Orchid think her son is in Vietnam?

3. CRITICAL THINKING How do you think Brave Orchid feels about her son?

4. Why does Brave Orchid feel sorry for the army and navy men?

5. READER RESPONSE Imagine that you are a soldier on your way to war. How do you think you would feel? Explain your answer.

Activity

DIRECTIONS: Where is Vietnam located? What are the people of this country like today? Do some research to discover more about this country. Create a travel poster showing interesting facts about Vietnam's people, geography, and cities to convince travelers to visit this beautiful nation.

UNIT 10

Interdisciplinary Connection 10

★ ★ ★ ★

History and Science

POLIO

One of the most devastating diseases of the early 1900s was poliomyelitis, or as it is more commonly called, polio. Polio is a viral infection that can affect any person at any age, although children tend to be more prone to it. It spreads easily by human contact. If the virus enters the central nervous system, it attacks the nerves that control motor activity and can cause paralysis. Usually the arms and legs are affected. In some cases, when paralysis affects the muscles of the throat and lungs, the disease can be fatal.

For years the word *polio* would strike fear into the hearts of parents. Outbreaks of polio occurred every year without warning. People would hear stories of children who suddenly came down with the disease and were left to a life in a wheelchair or an iron lung. The worst year for polio in the United States was 1952 when there were almost 58,000 cases reported and more than 3,000 deaths.

FINDING A VACCINE

The person who made polio a disease of the past was Jonas Salk. Salk, born in 1914, chose to go into research after medical school. During World War II, he helped to develop vaccines against influenza. After the war he became head of the viral research program at the University of Pittsburgh where he devoted his time to finding a polio vaccine. Salk wanted to make a vaccine that used killed viruses, rather than live viruses, because he thought killed viruses carried less risk of causing the disease it was supposed to prevent.

Salk tested his vaccine first on animals. In 1953 and 1954 more than 1 million schoolchildren received the vaccine. On April 22, 1955, it was announced that Salk had developed a vaccine that was "safe, effective, and potent." A nationwide effort followed to vaccinate all Americans. In 1960 Albert Sabin introduced an oral polio vaccine, which did not require an injection. Today most children receive the vaccine as infants. By 1962 the number of reported cases of polio had dropped to less than 1,000. Today polio is almost unheard of in the United States, and it is quickly disappearing in other parts of the world.

Salk's discovery made him a hero of the American people. But he was always very modest about his achievement. He noted, "I could have studied the . . . properties of, say, the tobacco mosaic virus, published my findings, and they would have been of some interest. But the fact that I chose to work on the polio virus, which brought control of a dreaded disease, made all the difference." Salk died in 1995 at the age of 80.

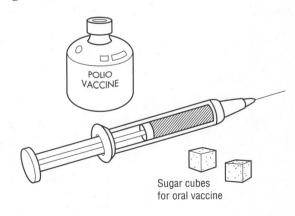

Sugar cubes for oral vaccine

(continued)

★ Interdisciplinary Connection 10

MAKING THE SCIENCE CONNECTION

DIRECTIONS: Recalling Facts Write the answers to the questions below in the space provided.

1. What is an infectious disease? _____

_____

2. What happens if the polio virus enters the central nervous system? _____

_____

_____

3. Why is polio no longer a major health problem in the United States? _____

_____

_____

4. What contribution did Albert Sabin make to eliminating polio? _____

_____

CRITICAL THINKING

5. What diseases are researchers working on today? _____

_____

_____

6. Many childhood diseases, such as measles, for which there are vaccines are

making comebacks recently. Why do you think this is so? _____

_____

_____

_____

Activity **DIRECTIONS: Conducting Interviews** Interview older adults, such as a grandparents, about health care in their youth. Ask them what diseases were common and what treatments were used. Ask them how medical science has changed in their lifetimes. Create a class list of the important medical breakthroughs and discoveries that are mentioned in your interviews.

Hands-On History Activity 10

Peanut Butter Mania

Try making peanut butter the old-fashioned way. **CAUTION:** Do not do this activity or eat peanut products if you have peanut allergies.

★ BACKGROUND

When the boll weevil, an insect that attacks cotton plants, damaged cotton crops after the Civil War, Southern farmers began to look for a substitute crop. They planted peanuts on more and more acres, and researchers looked for new uses for peanuts. In 1890 a doctor who was looking for an easily digestible form of protein for his patients made peanut butter, and the rest, as they say, is history. The peanut butter sandwich became a permanent part of the American diet. Of the 3 to 4 billion pounds of peanuts the United States produces each year, half become peanut butter. Even if you don't live in one of the major peanut-producing states of Georgia, Alabama, North Carolina, Texas, Oklahoma, Virginia, and Florida, you can make your own peanut butter. Try making two different batches and compare the results.

★ MATERIALS

- blender or food processor
- heavy rolling pin
- two 1-quart self-sealing plastic bags
- spatula
- plastic container with lid

★ INGREDIENTS FOR EACH BATCH

- 1 cup shelled peanuts
- 1½ tablespoons peanut oil
- ½ teaspoon salt
- crackers or celery
- 1 teaspoon cinnamon (optional)
- ¼ cup honey (optional)

FASCINATING FACTS

Peanut oil is used to make soaps and paints. The shells are used to make plastics, wallboard, and abrasives.

Hands-On History Activity 10

UNIT 10

★ WHAT TO DO

A. Batch One: Place the peanuts in a blender. Blend for about one minute, or until peanuts are finely chopped. Add the oil and salt and blend until smooth. **Batch Two:** Put a cup of peanuts into a plastic bag. Close the bag securely. Then place that bag inside another bag, so your peanuts are double bagged. Use the rolling pin to crush the peanuts inside the plastic bag, rolling until they are crushed. Then open the bags and add the oil and salt. Try to remove as much air as possible from the bag. Continue rolling until the peanut butter is of spreading consistency.

B. Try your peanut butter on a cracker or celery stick. Place the remaining peanut butter into covered containers. Refrigerate immediately to prevent oil separation. Stir well before using to get the best consistency and taste.

C. You can add ¼ cup of honey after grinding the nuts. Just blend into the peanut butter. Or you can try adding a teaspoon of cinnamon to the peanut butter for a different taste. Keep notes of how these ingredients affected the taste and texture of your peanut butter.

ACTIVITY REPORT

DIRECTIONS: Answer the following questions in the space provided.

1. How much peanut butter did you make from 1 cup of peanuts? _____

2. How would you describe the peanut butter made by each method? _____

_____

_____

3. Did you add honey to either batch of peanut butter? If so, did it change the texture of the peanut butter? _____

_____

4. How would you describe the differences between your peanut butters and the peanut butter you buy? _____

_____

5. How do you think making peanut butter commercially affected peanut butter's popularity? _____

★ ★ ★ ★ ★ ★ ★ ★ ★ ★ ★ ★

History Simulations and Problem Solving **10**—Teaching Strategy

★ Arguing *Brown* v. *Board of Education of Topeka, Kansas*

Topic

In its May 17, 1954, decision in the case of *Brown* v. *Board of Education of Topeka, Kansas* the United States Supreme Court ruled that segregated schools are unconstitutional.

Objective

Acting as lawyers and justices in a mock oral argument before the Supreme Court, students will explore the civil rights issues in *Brown* v. *Board of Education of Topeka, Kansas.*

Materials

- Reproduce the preparation sheets on pages 16 and 17 (one copy of the appropriate preparation sheet per attorney; one copy of both sheets to justices).

- Reproduce the opinion form on page 18 (one copy per justice).

- Reproduce the decision sheet on page 19 (for all students to use as follow-up to the trial).

Procedure

1. Organize the class into three groups: the the NAACP lawyers representing Linda Brown and the other students appealing the lower court decisions; the lawyers representing the various boards of education (who want the lower court decisions to be affirmed); and nine Supreme Court justices.

2. Present the basic facts of the *Brown* v. *Board of Education of Topeka, Kansas* case. Give each lawyer a copy of the appropriate preparation sheet (pages 16 and 17). Give teams two weeks to research the case. In the week before the trial, allow students 10 minutes at the start of each class to meet with their groups and discuss their findings.

3. Ask the nine justices to choose one student to act as chief justice. Encourage the justices to review both sides of the case to evaluate the information presented during the trial. Explain that the job of Supreme Court justices is to decide the meaning of the Constitution, our highest law—not to decide questions of right or wrong. Student justices will need to decide if the Constitution permits or prohibits segregation.

4. Explain that Supreme Court cases have no witnesses. Lawyers do all of the talking. They often spend months or years preparing their cases before presenting their arguments. Invite each team of attorneys to select a lead lawyer (take the role of Thurgood Marshall or John W. Davis) who will present the group's case.

   Allow both teams time to formulate their arguments and prepare written statements. These persuasive arguments should include references to the specific students' cases being argued, and take no longer than five minutes to read aloud. Lead attorneys should rehearse their statements before the entire team and encourage input of all group members.

5. On the day of the simulation, have the nine justices sit in a row at the front of the classroom. After the chief justice introduces the case, the lead lawyer for the Brown's case stands and reads his or her statement. Then the lead lawyer for the Board of Education stands and reads his or her statement.

UNIT 10

History Simulations and Problem Solving 10—Teaching Strategy

6. The justices ask both lawyers questions about the case. Lead lawyers should consult briefly with their team before answering. Explain to students that in the real Supreme Court, justices may ask questions even while lawyers are presenting their statements. Some lawyers have complained that they were unable to finish their statements because the Court used up their time with so many questions!

7. After all of the justices' questions have been answered, allow them time to confer together in another room. Give each justice a copy of the opinion form. After answering the questions on the form and discussing both sides of the case, the justices vote on a final decision. If all nine justices agree, they write a joint, unanimous decision. If they disagree, the majority writes one opinion, and the minority writes a dissenting opinion.

8. After the opinions have been written, the Court reconvenes. The chief justice reads aloud the majority opinion, and, if time permits, the dissenting opinion, too.

Background

Throughout the United States in the 1950s, African American students and their parents were angered over the inequality of education resulting from school segregation:

- Seven year old Linda Brown had to walk across railroad tracks and ride an old bus to a run-down African American school, although there was a much better white school just five blocks from her home in Topeka, Kansas.

- Harry and Liza Briggs' five children attended African American schools in Clarendon County, South Carolina, which operated on one-fourth the amount of money given to white schools. The county spent $43 a year on each African American student and $179 a year on each white student.

- In Farmville, Virginia, 16 year old Barbara Johns led her fellow high school students on a strike for a better school. Moton High School had been built for 200 students, but held 450. There was no cafeteria and no gym. The highest-paid teachers at Moton received less than the lowest-paid teachers at Farmville's white schools.

Lawyers for the National Association for the Advancement of Colored People (NAACP) used these cases to argue that school segregation was unconstitutional. Each case was defeated in lower courts, but the NAACP appealed to the United States Supreme Court. There they were grouped together with two other cases as *Brown* v. *Board of Education of Topeka*. Linda Brown and the others represented by the NAACP were appealing a lower court decision to the Supreme Court.

In December 1952 Thurgood Marshall and the NAACP lawyers presented two arguments to the Supreme Court. First, Marshall argued that segregation laws denied African Americans "equal protection of laws" as guaranteed by the Fourteenth Amendment. He believed that the Fourteenth Amendment made the 1896 *Plessy* v. *Ferguson* doctrine of "separate but equal" unconstitutional. This decision had established that communities could provide African Americans with separate facilities as long as the facilities were equal to those of whites. Second, Marshall argued that segregated schools can never be truly equal because separating people makes them feel unequal and inferior.

(continued)

★ ★ ★ ★ ★ ★ ★ ★ ★ ★ ★

History Simulations and Problem Solving 10—Teaching Strategy

John W. Davis was the lead attorney for the Board of Education—those who won the cases in the lower courts and wanted the Supreme Court to affirm, or leave alone, those decisions. Davis argued that nothing in the Constitution prevented separation, as long as facilities were equal. He tried to persuade the Court that each state has the right to make its own decisions on social matters such as segregation. Davis believed that the *Plessy* v. *Ferguson* decision was constitutional.

The Decision The justices took their time to reach a decision in this very difficult case. Finally, on May 17, 1954, the Supreme Court unanimously ruled that segregated schools "are inherently unequal." In its decision, the Court stated, "We conclude, unanimously, that in the field of education the doctrine of 'separate but equal' has no place." The Court explained that even if separate schools for African Americans and whites had the same physical facilities, no true equality existed as long as segregation itself existed. To separate African American children "solely because of their race," the Court wrote, "generates a feeling of inferiority as to their status in the community that may affect their hearts and minds in a way very unlikely ever to be undone."

With All Deliberate Speed The Court ordered that communities work to desegregate their schools "with all deliberate speed." In some communities, compliance was relatively quick and painless. Far more often, however, strong local resistance produced long delays. By the fall of 1957, only 684 of 3,000 affected school districts in the South had even begun to desegregate. Despite the opposition of many whites, the *Brown* v. *Board of Education of Topeka, Kansas* decision gave great hope to African Americans. It provided a way to attack segregation—in the classroom and beyond.

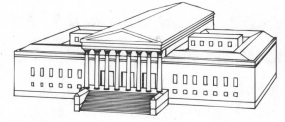

Follow-Up

Review the mock oral argument with your class. Photocopy and distribute the decision sheet (page 19). Encourage discussion by asking the following questions.

- What did you find to be the most difficult part of preparing a case for the Supreme Court? Why?

- How was the student justices' decision similar to or different from the actual historic opinion?

- Why did the real justices base their opinion on the Fourteenth Amendment?

- If you were to reargue this case, what might you do differently?

Critical Thinking

Have students think about the results of their simulation. Then have them answer these questions, orally or in writing.

1. Why do you think it was important that *Brown* v. *Board of Education of Topeka, Kansas* was a unanimous decision? How do you think Americans might have reacted if the Court had split?

2. Why do you think most Southerners responded more negatively to the Court's decision than most Northerners?

3. Why is the *Brown* v. *Board of Education of Topeka, Kansas* decision regarded as a landmark Court decision?

4. What desegregation problems are there in today's schools?

UNIT 10

History Simulations and Problem Solving 10

UNIT 10

Arguing *Brown* v. *Board of Education of Topeka, Kansas*

PREPARING THE STUDENTS' AND PARENTS' CASE

SITUATION

On December 9, 1952, the United States Supreme Court in Washington, D.C., heard arguments in the *Brown* v. *Board of Education of Topeka, Kansas* case. All of the seats were filled in the court chamber, and 400 people were turned away. Thurgood Marshall, the great-grandson of an enslaved African American, argued for the students and parents appealing the lower court decisions. Marshall had argued 15 cases before the Supreme Court—and won 13. John W. Davis was the opposing attorney. Some people said that Davis, who had argued more cases before the Supreme Court than any other living attorney, was the best lawyer in America.

DIRECTIONS: Following are some questions to keep in mind as you research your case. Note your findings on the lines provided. After finishing your research, write a statement on a separate sheet of paper, presenting your case before the Supreme Court. You must convince the justices that segregated schools are unconstitutional.

- Why are your clients suing the Board of Education of Topeka, Kansas?

  _____

  _____

- Why are your clients suing the Clarendon County, South Carolina, school board?

  _____

  _____

- What did the Supreme Court decide in the 1896 *Plessy* v. *Ferguson* case? How will

  you mention this case in your statement? _____

  _____

- Does the Constitution permit segregation? How can you use the Fourteenth

  Amendment to support your case? _____

  _____

  _____

  _____

(continued)

History Simulations and Problem Solving 10

PREPARING THE BOARD OF EDUCATION'S CASE

SITUATION

On December 9, 1952, the United States Supreme Court in Washington, D.C., heard arguments in the *Brown* v. *Board of Education of Topeka, Kansas* case. All of the seats were filled in the court chamber, and 400 people were turned away. Thurgood Marshall, the great-grandson of an enslaved African American, argued for the students and parents appealing the lower court decisions. Marshall had argued 15 cases before the Supreme Court—and won 13. John W. Davis was the opposing attorney. Some people said that Davis, who had argued more cases before the Supreme Court than any other living attorney, was the best lawyer in America.

DIRECTIONS: Following are some questions to keep in mind as you research your case. Note your findings on the lines provided. After finishing your research, write a statement on a separate sheet of paper, presenting your case before the Supreme Court. You must convince the justices that segregated schools are constitutional.

• How do you hope the Supreme Court will view the lower court decisions in the

case of Linda Brown and the other students? _____

_____

• What arguments can you anticipate that the students and parents will likely make,

which you will need to argue against? _____

_____

• What did the Supreme Court decide in the 1896 *Plessy* v. *Ferguson* case? How will

you mention this case in your statement? _____

_____

• Does the Constitution specifically outlaw segregation? _____

_____

• What does the Fourteenth Amendment say? How does this affect your case?

_____

_____

(continued)

History Simulations and Problem Solving 10

UNIT 10

OPINION FORM FOR THE JUSTICES

DIRECTIONS: Following are some questions to keep in mind as you decide the *Brown* v. *Board of Education of Topeka, Kansas* case. Note your responses on the lines provided. After discussing the case with the other justices, take a vote. If the decision is unanimous, or undivided, write a joint opinion as a group. If any of the justices disagree, then both a majority opinion and a dissenting opinion will need to be written.

• What were the essential arguments of the students and parents? _____

_____

• What were the essential arguments of the board of education? _____

_____

_____

• In your opinion did the students' and parents' attorneys prove that segregation is unconstitutional and that the lower court rulings should be overturned? Why or why not?

_____

_____

_____

_____

_____

_____

_____

_____

_____

_____

_____

_____

_____

(continued)

DECISION SHEET

Brown et al. v. Board of Education of Topeka et al.

In approaching this problem, we cannot turn the clock back to 1868 when the [Fourteenth] Amendment was adopted, or even to 1896 when *Plessy* v. *Ferguson* was written. We must consider public education in the light of its full development and its present place in American life throughout the Nation. Only in this way can it be determined if segregation in public schools deprives these plaintiffs of the equal protection of the laws.

Today, education is perhaps the most important function of state and local governments. Compulsory school attendance laws and the great expenditures for education both demonstrate our recognition of the importance of education to our democratic society. It is required in the performance of our most basic public responsibilities, even service in the armed forces. It is the very foundation of good citizenship. Today it is a principal instrument in awakening the child to cultural values, in preparing him for later professional training, and in helping him to adjust normally to his environment. In these days it is doubtful that any child may reasonably be expected to succeed in life if he is denied the opportunity of an education. Such an opportunity where the state has undertaken to provide it, is a right which must be made available to all on equal terms.

We come then to the question presented: Does segregation of children in public schools solely on the basis of race, even though the physical facilities and other "tangible" factors may be equal, deprive the children of the minority group of equal educational opportunities? We believe that it does. . . .

We conclude, unanimously, that in the field of public education the doctrine of "separate but equal" has no place. Separate educational facilities are inherently unequal.

—Excerpt from the United States Supreme Court opinion delivered by Chief Justice Earl Warren, 1954.

Chapter 27 Resources

★ **Vocabulary Activity 27**

DIRECTIONS: Matching Select the term that matches each definition below. Write the correct term in the space provided.

allege	demilitarized zone	censure	subversion	airlift
stalemate	containment	perjury	blacklist	inflation

1. The policy to stop expansion of another country _____

2. An operation in which cargo planes fly food, fuel, and supplies into an area; one took place in Berlin in 1948 _____

3. A rise in prices _____

4. A situation in which neither side is able to gain much ground or achieve a decisive victory _____

5. A region where military forces could not enter _____

6. Sabotage _____

7. Document with the names of individuals whose loyalty to the United States was suspicious _____

8. Lying under oath _____

9. Declare without proof _____

10. Formally criticize _____

DIRECTIONS: Writing Explanations Explain the meaning of the phrases by answering the questions. Write the answers on a separate sheet of paper.

11. The iron curtain was not made of iron nor did it hang at any window. What was the **iron curtain**? Who coined the phrase?

12. In the Cold War, there was no actual fighting, nor did it take place in a cold climate. What was the **Cold War**? Who participated in it?

13. A closed shop was not a store that had gone out of business. What was a **closed shop**?

★ **Chapter Skills Activity 27**

CHAPTER 27

Making Inferences

Inferences are made by using previous knowledge plus the information presented to draw conclusions. When you read something with an implied meaning, it is necessary to make an inference. Often a subject is only implied and the reader must decide what the author meant.

DIRECTIONS: Read through the passage carefully. Think about what the author meant by some of the words. Then answer the questions on a separate sheet of paper.

> I pledge allegiance to the Flag of the United States of America and to the Republic for which it stands, one Nation under God, indivisible, with liberty and justice for all.

Francis Bellamy wrote the Pledge of Allegiance in 1892 for the 400th anniversary of Columbus's landing. In 1954 the words "under God" were added at President Dwight D. Eisenhower's urging.

1. The Civil War ended in 1865. Do you think the author was implying anything by adding "one Nation"?

_____

2. Think about civil rights at the time this was written. What can you infer from the word *equality* not being used?

_____

3. What do you think is implied with the word *republic* being capitalized?

_____

4. What inferences can you make about President Eisenhower based on the words he wanted in the pledge?

_____

Activity **DIRECTIONS:** Find a recent copy of your local newspaper. Look for an article that discusses a topic you know about. Create a two-column chart on a separate sheet of paper. Then write facts that are clearly stated in one column and facts that are implied in the other column.

| Critical Thinking Skills Activity 27 | Analyzing Primary Sources |

Analyzing Primary Sources

SOCIAL STUDIES OBJECTIVE: Use primary sources to acquire information about the United States

LEARNING THE SKILL

When you use primary sources, you are using historical materials that are firsthand accounts. Such sources allow you to learn about events directly from the people who experienced them. Historians often use primary sources to write about the past.

FROM THE INTERNAL SECURITY ACT OF 1950

. . . In the United States, those individuals who knowingly and willfully participate in the world Communist movement . . . in effect repudiate [throw away] their allegiance to the United States. . . .

. . . The Communist network in the United States is inspired and controlled . . . by foreign agents who are sent into the United States . . . [and] who use their diplomatic . . . status as a shield. . . .

. . . One device for infiltration [entrance] by Communists is by procuring naturalization [getting citizenship] for disloyal aliens who use their citizenship as a badge for admission into . . . our society.

. . . Congress. . . [must] enact appropriate legislation . . . designed to prevent . . . [the Communist Party] from accomplishing its purpose in the United States. . . .

FROM THE COMMUNIST CONTROL ACT OF 1954

. . . The Congress hereby finds and declares that the Communist Party of the United States, although purportedly [supposedly] a political party, is in fact an instrumentality of conspiracy to overthrow the Government of the United States. . . . Therefore, the Communist Party should be outlawed.

. . . The Communist Party of the United States . . . [is] not entitled to any of the rights [and] privileges . . . attendant upon [other] legal bodies created under the laws of the United States. . . .

. . . Whoever . . . becomes . . . a member of . . . the Communist Party . . . shall be subject to all the . . . penalties of the Internal Security Act of 1950. . . . In determining membership . . . in the Communist Party . . . [a] jury . . . shall consider evidence . . . as to whether the accused person:

1) Has been listed . . . as a member . . .
2) Has made financial contribution . . .
4) Has executed orders, plans, or directives . . . of the organization.
6) Has conferred [discussed] with . . . members of the organization . . .
8) Has written, spoken or . . . communicated . . . orders . . . or plans of the organization.
9) Has prepared documents, pamphlets, leaflets, books . . . in behalf . . . of the organization.
10) Has mailed, shipped [or] . . . delivered . . . material . . . in behalf of the organization.

APPLYING THE SKILL

DIRECTIONS: Use the passages to answer the following questions.

1. What was the problem the United States government tried to deal with in these two acts?

_____

_____

CHAPTER 27

Critical Thinking Skills Activity 27 | Analyzing Primary Sources

2. Why did the government consider the problem serious?

_____

_____

3. How was the Communist Party of the United States to have been treated, according to the Communist Control Act of 1954?

_____

_____

4. Do these sources provide you with an accurate account of the threat of communism in the United States? Explain your answer.

_____

_____

PRACTICING THE SKILL

DIRECTIONS: In the blank at the left, write the letter of the choice that best answers the question.

_____ **1.** Which of the following groups could the Internal Security Act of 1950 have harmed by labeling their members as Communists?
   A. churches
   B. government leaders and foreign agents
   C. diplomats and naturalized citizens
   D. Congress and diplomats

_____ **2.** What primary source would a historian reading the Communist Control Act of 1954 have to consult to find the penalties for becoming a member of the Communist Party during the 1950s?
   A. the United States Constitution
   B. the Communist Control Act of 1954
   C. the Bill of Rights
   D. the Internal Security Act of 1950

_____ **3.** The Internal Security Act and the Communist Control Act placed limits on which constitutional right?
   A. the right to join a political party of one's choosing
   B. the right to worship as one pleases
   C. the right to vote
   D. the right to a trial by jury

Name _____ Date _____ Class _____

Divided Europe—NATO and the Warsaw Pact Nations, 1955

Legend:
- NATO
- Warsaw Pact
- Nonaligned nations

0   125   250 miles
0   125   250 kilometers

DIRECTIONS: Write your answers to questions 1–4 on the map. You may abbreviate if you wish.

1. Identify the NATO country that is farthest east and label it "farthest east."

2. Determine how many NATO countries and how many Warsaw Pact countries are shown on the map. Write these numbers over the appropriate regions of the map.

3. Use red to color the Warsaw Pact nations that bordered NATO nations.

4. Identify the nonaligned nations. Use blue to color the nonaligned nations.

5. Use the map to explain why you think NATO and the Warsaw Pact were organized.

_____

_____

_____

★ **Time Line Activity 27**

Anti-Communist Backlash in the United States

DIRECTIONS: Use the following information about events occurring during the anti-Communist backlash in the United States to create your own time line. Then add the World Events to the time line. Include the date for each event.

THE RED SCARE IN THE UNITED STATES

1955

1953

1951

1949

1947

★ Background

In the late 1940s fears of Communist subversion led to congressional investigations on un-American activities. This Red Scare reached its peak with McCarthyism. Senator Joseph McCarthy used highly publicized personal attacks to discredit people thought to be subversive. In 1947 the House Un-American Activities Committee (HUAC) presented evidence against the Hollywood Ten, screenwriters and directors accused of having Communist affiliations. A year later, congressional hearings on Alger Hiss began. An admitted spy accused Hiss of giving him secret State Department documents to pass on to the Soviets. In 1950 Senator McCarthy declared that the State Department was riddled with card-carrying members of the Communist Party. Julius and Ethel Rosenberg were brought to trial in 1951 for spying for the Soviet Union. The Rosenbergs were executed in 1953. The nationally televised Army-McCarthy hearings in 1954 failed to substantiate McCarthy's claims of Communist penetration of the army.

THE RED SCARE IN THE UNITED STATES

- HUAC began its hearings on the Hollywood Ten.
- Alger Hiss was accused of passing secret government documents to a Soviet spy.
- Senator McCarthy claimed that the State Department was riddled with Communist Party members.
- The Rosenbergs were brought to trial for spying for the Soviet Union.
- The Army-McCarthy hearings were televised.

WORLD EVENTS

- In 1955 the Soviet Union signed the Warsaw Pact.

CHAPTER 27

Linking Past and Present Activity 27

Computers

 In 1946 ENIAC (Electronic Numerical Integrator and Computer) became the first general-purpose electronic digital computer. The 30-ton machine was huge—more than 100 feet long and 10 feet high. ENIAC had more than 18,000 glass electronic vacuum tubes and could perform complex mathematical calculations. It computed at speeds of 1,000 to 5,000 additions per second.

Although ENIAC was a modern miracle for its time, it was also expensive and huge. Its vacuum tubes heated up and burned out. The invention of transistors in 1948 solved this problem. Transistors are electronic devices made from silicon, a material found in common sand. Two hundred transistors fit in the same space as one vacuum tube. Transistors produced no heat, did not burn out, eliminated miles of wiring, were very small, and were inexpensive to produce. Computers with transistors could compute 500,000 additions per second.

 Today computers are smaller, faster, and more reliable than ever before.

In 1961 the first integrated circuits were sold. Integrated circuits contain many miniature electronic transistors on a single, tiny silicon microchip. In 1964, 10 transistor circuits were on a chip. By 1969, a thousand transistors fit on a single chip. Today a microchip tiny enough to pass through the eye of a sewing needle may contain more than a million circuit lines and transistors—10 times the electrical components of the 30-ton ENIAC.

Microprocessors have made it possible for handheld calculators to be more powerful than ENIAC. Personal computers for home use also use microprocessor technology. Supercomputers and the Internet provide researchers all over the world with access to more data and better ways to explore, analyze, manipulate, visualize, store, and interact with that data.

CHAPTER 27

Activity

DIRECTIONS: Media Literacy Many people contributed to the development of modern computers. Use the media center to research these pioneers and summarize their contributions to computing.

Contributors to Modern Personal Computing

Person	Contribution
Jack S. Kilby	
Grace Murray Hopper	
William (Bill) Gates III	
Steven P. Jobs	
Paul Barans	

★ Primary Source Reading 27

Winston Churchill Speaks to Americans

> ✪ **Interpreting the Source** Winston Churchill, Britain's prime minister, gave his "iron curtain" speech in Fulton, Missouri, on March 5, 1946. As you read this excerpt, think about why the iron curtain brought fear to the victors of war.

A shadow has fallen upon the scenes so lately lighted by the Allied victory. Nobody knows what Soviet Russia and its Communist international organisation intends to do in the immediate future, or what are the limits, if any, to their expansive and proselytising [converting] tendencies. . . .

From Stettin in the Baltic to Trieste in the Adriatic, an iron curtain has descended across the Continent. Behind that line lie all the capitals of the ancient states of Central and Eastern Europe. Warsaw, Berlin, Prague, Vienna, Budapest, Belgrade, Bucharest and Sofia, all these famous cities and the populations around them lie in what I must call the Soviet sphere, and all are subject in one form or another, not only to Soviet influence but to a very high and, in many cases, increasing measure of control from Moscow. . . .

. . . I do not believe that Soviet Russia desires war. What they desire is the fruits of war and the indefinite expansion of their power and doctrines. But what we have to consider here to-day while time remains, is the permanent prevention of war and the establishment of conditions of freedom and democracy as rapidly as possible in all countries. . . .

. . . There never was a war in all history easier to prevent by timely action than the one which has just desolated such great areas of the globe. It could have been prevented in my belief without the firing of a single shot, and Germany might be powerful, prosperous and honoured to-day; but no one would listen and one by one we were all sucked into the awful whirlpool. We surely must not let that happen again. This can only be achieved by reaching now, in 1946, a good understanding on all points with Russia under the general authority of the United Nations Organisation and by the maintenance of that good understanding through many peaceful years. . . . There is the solution which I respectfully offer to you in this Address to which I have given the title "The Sinews of Peace." . . .

SOURCE: *The Sinews of Peace: Post-War Speeches by Winston S. Churchill.* Boston: Houghton Mifflin Company, 1949.

DOCUMENT-BASED QUESTION

DIRECTIONS: Answer the following question on a separate sheet of paper.
What do you think Churchill is trying to imply by the phrase "Soviet sphere"?

DIRECTIONS: Making a Map Make a map of Europe to show the iron curtain that Churchill refers to. Include the cities that are listed in the second paragraph of this excerpt.

Chapter 27 Section Resources

★ | **Guided Reading Activity 27-1**

DIRECTIONS: Recalling the Facts Use the information in your textbook to answer the questions. Use another sheet of paper if necessary.

1. Who were the Big Three leaders? _____

2. Where did the Big Three meet in February 1945? _____

3. What were the terms of the agreement that came out of that meeting? _____

_____

4. How was Germany to be divided and controlled? _____

5. When and where was the charter signed forming the United Nations? _____

_____

6. What two camps did Europe split into? _____

7. Who first used the term "iron curtain?" What did he mean?

_____

8. What policy did George F. Kennan's ideas about Soviet expansion lead to?

_____

9. What was the Truman Doctrine? _____

10. Who proposed a plan to provide massive economic aid to Europe? What was this

plan called? _____

11. Why did Joseph Stalin create the Berlin blockade on June 24, 1948? _____

_____

12. How did President Harry S Truman save West Berlin? _____

13. What two nations did Germany become in October 1949? _____

14. What did the crisis in Berlin confirm? _____

15. What divided Europe into two armed camps? _____

16. How did the UN propose to settle the dispute over Palestine? _____

_____

17. Who led the Chinese Communist forces in China's civil war? How did the

war end? _____

SECTION 27-1

★ **Guided Reading Activity 27-2**

DIRECTIONS: Outlining Locate the heading in your textbook. Then use the information under the heading to help you write each answer. Use another sheet of paper if necessary.

I. The Postwar Economy

    A. Introduction—What caused prices to surge after the war? _____

    B. Workers Seek Higher Wages—What happened when employers refused to

    raise wages? _____

    _____

    C. Truman Takes Action— How did President Harry S Truman force striking

    miners back to work and help them at the same time? _____

II. Truman Faces the Republicans

    A. Republicans Control Congress

      1. What slogan helped the Republicans win control of Congress in 1946?

      _____

      2. What bill did Congress introduce in 1947 to limit the power of labor unions?

      _____

    B. The Election of 1948—How did Truman campaign against Thomas Dewey,

    who was leading in the polls? _____

    C. A Fair Deal for Americans—What laws from Truman's Fair Deal did Congress

    pass after the election? _____

III. A Stand on Civil Rights

    A. What steps did Harry S Truman take to advance the civil rights of

    African Americans? _____

    B. What else did Truman propose in his domestic agenda?

    _____

★ Guided Reading Activity 27-3

DIRECTIONS: Filling in the Blanks Use your textbook to fill in the blanks using the words in the box. Some words may be used twice. Use another sheet of paper if necessary.

General Douglas MacArthur	**"police action"**	**Seoul**	**Inchon**
demilitarized zone	**Pyongyang**	**July 27, 1953**	**stalemate**
United Nations	**38th parallel**	**containment**	**Chinese**
Chinese troops	**June 25, 1950**		

Conflict in Korea

At the end of World War II, the United States and the Soviet Union divided Korea in half along the **(1)** _____ of latitude. The Soviets controlled North Korea, and the Americans controlled South Korea. On **(2)** _____ the armies of North Korea crossed the 38th parallel into South Korea, intending to unify the country by force. Without asking Congress, Harry S Truman ordered the use of limited American air and sea forces in Korea. He called this **(3)** _____ necessary to carry out America's policy of **(4)** _____. The **(5)** _____ agreed to send a special force to the region under the United States's direction. Truman appointed **(6)** _____ as commander. In September, UN forces took the city of **(7)** _____ and moved to recapture **(8)** _____. By October 1, North Koreans were forced to retreat. On October 19, the UN forces captured **(9)** _____, the North Korean capital. As the UN forces moved northward, Truman ignored a warning from the **(10)** _____ that it would send its army to support the North Koreans. On November 26, huge numbers of **(11)** _____ attacked UN forces. Within weeks the Communists had recaptured **(12)** _____.

American Leadership Divided

By January 1951, the war had become a **(13)** _____ which lasted for almost two years. When **(14)** _____ and Truman disagreed over tactics in Korea, Truman relieved MacArthur of his command in Korea. On **(15)** _____, a cease-fire agreement ended the Korean War. This agreement created a **(16)** _____ between North and South Korea.

SECTION 27-3

★ Guided Reading Activity 27-4

DIRECTIONS: Recalling the Facts use the information in your textbook to answer the questions. Use another sheet of paper if necessary.

1. What fear did the Cold War intensify? _____

2. What term was used for people who were friendly to Communists?

   _____

3. What was the fear that Communists had penetrated all levels of American society

   and were attempting to weaken the government? _____

4. What did the McCarran Act require? _____

5. What congressional committee began investigating Communist subversion in the

   nation in 1947? _____

6. What did the committee's actions fuel in the nation? _____

7. Who were the "Hollywood Ten"? _____

8. What were blacklists and how were they used? _____

   _____

9. Whom did Whittaker Chambers, a spy for the Soviet Union, accuse of also being

   a spy? _____

10. Who were Julius and Ethel Rosenberg? _____

    _____

11. How did the Rosenbergs' trial end? _____

12. What was *McCarthyism*? _____

13. What happened as a result of Joseph McCarthy's four-year long congressional

    investigation? _____

14. How did McCarthy's subcommittee treat people it called to testify?

    _____

15. Why did McCarthyism work? _____

16. When did the Senate vote to censure McCarthy? _____

★ Reteaching Activity 27-1

DIRECTIONS: Determining Cause and Effect Each cause leading to the Cold War had its own series of effects. The numbered items list these effects. Complete the diagram by writing the numbers of the effects for each cause on the lines.

1. The 2 million citizens of West Berlin were cut off from vital supplies.

2. Civil war raged in Greece.

3. The Soviet Union entered the war against Japan.

4. NATO was formed.

5. Joseph Stalin promised free elections in occupied Eastern Europe.

6. Congress approved the Marshall Plan.

7. Winston Churchill declared that an "iron curtain" had descended on Europe.

8. The Warsaw Pact was established.

9. American and British cargo planes flew into West Berlin day and night for 10 months.

10. The Soviet Union received territory in Asia.

11. Germany was officially divided into two nations.

12. The United Nations was planned.

13. NSC-68 was released.

14. Germany was divided into four zones.

15. The United States established a policy of containment.

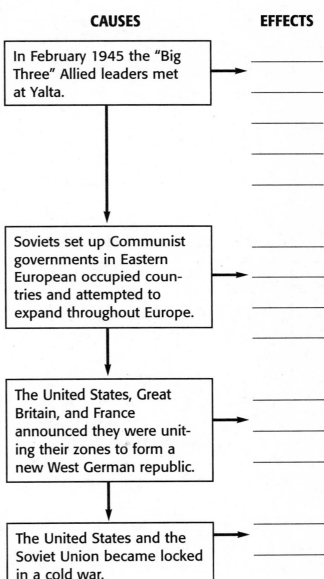

CAUSES

In February 1945 the "Big Three" Allied leaders met at Yalta.

EFFECTS

Soviets set up Communist governments in Eastern European occupied countries and attempted to expand throughout Europe.

The United States, Great Britain, and France announced they were uniting their zones to form a new West German republic.

The United States and the Soviet Union became locked in a cold war.

SECTION 27-1

★ **Reteaching Activity 27-2**

SECTION 27-2

DIRECTIONS: Organizing Facts The items in the Fact Bank provide details about the nation's economy after World War II, along with proposals made by Harry S Truman and the Republican Congress to solve some of the problems related to the economy. Complete the diagram by writing the number of each item in the correct box.

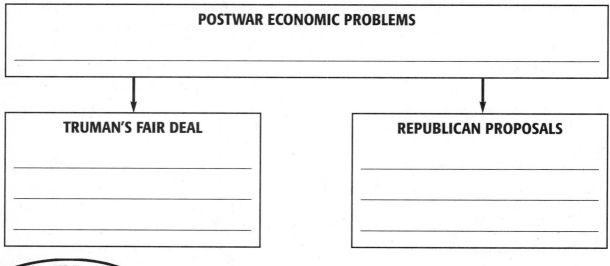

POSTWAR ECONOMIC PROBLEMS

TRUMAN'S FAIR DEAL

REPUBLICAN PROPOSALS

★**FACT BANK**

1. Expand Social Security benefits
2. President Truman forces striking miners back on the job.
3. Create a system of national health insurance
4. Reverse policies set by FDR's New Deal
5. Increase federal spending to create jobs
6. Limit government spending
7. Labor unions strike.
8. Control labor unions
9. Rapid price increases and consumer demands cause inflation.
10. Raise minimum wage
11. Reduce government regulations of the economy
12. Provide funds for new public housing
13. Workers demand wage increases.
14. Taft-Hartley bill

DIRECTIONS: Essay On a separate sheet of paper, answer the following questions.

15. Why did the *Chicago Daily Tribune* issue a special edition announcing "Dewey Defeats Truman" the morning following the election of 1948? What actually happened in the election?

16. How did Truman attempt to help "every segment of our population and every individual" with civil rights and domestic agenda proposals?

★ **Reteaching Activity 27-3**

DIRECTIONS: **Sequencing Events** Number the events in the order in which they occurred. Write the same number for events that occurred at the same time.

_____ **A.** UN forces take the port of Inchon and then recapture Seoul.

_____ **B.** Huge numbers of Chinese troops attack UN forces, forcing UN forces to retreat south back across the 38th parallel.

_____ **C.** Harry S Truman asks the United Nations to send forces to South Korea.

_____ **D.** Truman fires General Douglas MacArthur.

_____ **E.** The United States and the Soviet Union divide the Korean Peninsula in half along the 38th parallel.

_____ **F.** The UN forces capture the North Korean capital of Pyongyang and move north toward the Yalu River.

_____ **G.** A cease-fire agreement establishes a demilitarized zone between North and South Korea.

_____ **H.** Truman immediately employs police action in South Korea.

_____ **I.** China warns the United States that it will support North Korea.

_____ **J.** MacArthur complains to Congress when Truman refuses to bomb Chinese troops stationed in North Korea.

_____ **K.** MacArthur assures Truman that neither China nor the Soviet Union will interfere with an invasion of North Korea.

_____ **L.** After the UN forces retake Seoul, the war enters a two-year stalemate.

_____ **M.** Communist forces from North Korea cross the 38th parallel with the intention of unifying Korea by force; within days they capture Seoul.

_____ **N.** The Communists recapture Seoul.

_____ **O.** General MacArthur leads American troops to stop the Communist advance into South Korea.

SECTION 27-3

DIRECTIONS: **Essay** On a separate sheet of paper, answer the questions below.

Why did President Harry S Truman relieve General Douglas MacArthur of his command in Korea? What was the public's reaction?

★ **Reteaching Activity 27-4**

DIRECTIONS: Completing a Cluster Each of the numbered items in the Fact Bank explains a term or name in the cluster. Write the correct numbers in the blanks to complete the cluster.

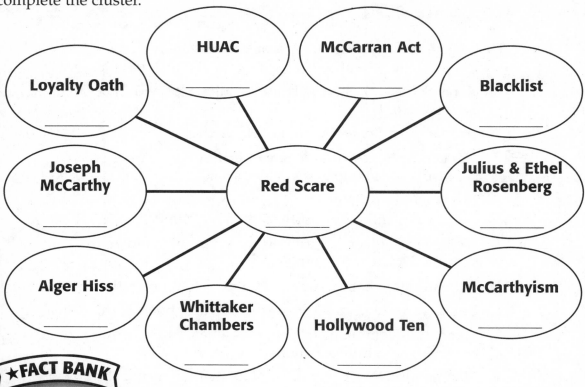

★**FACT BANK**

1. convicted of plotting to pass secrets about the atomic bomb to the Soviet Union; executed in 1953

2. committee that investigated Communist subversion in the nation

3. magazine editor who admitted to spying

4. document with names of individuals whose loyalty to the nation was suspicious

5. senator whose brutal hunt for Communists destroyed the career of many innocent Americans

6. statement swearing allegiance to the United States

7. the use of unproved accusations against political opponents

8. fear that Communist spies and sympathizers had penetrated all levels of American society and were attempting to weaken the government

9. required all Communist organizations to register with the government and to provide lists of members

10. alleged spy for the Soviet Union; convicted only of perjury

11. screenwriters and directors who went to jail for refusing to answer questions about their political beliefs

★ Enrichment Activity 27-1

Representatives to the United Nations

The United States was among the 50 nations that initiated the United Nations. Study the chart that lists some of the United States representatives to the United Nations.

United States Representatives to the United Nations

Year	Representative	Year	Representative	Year	Representative
1947	Warren R. Austin	1969	Charles W. Yost	1981	Jeanne J. Kirkpatrick
1953	Henry Cabot Lodge, Jr.	1971	George H. W. Bush	1985	Vernon A. Walters
1960	James J. Wadsworth	1973	John A. Scali	1989	Thomas R. Pickering
1961	Adlai E. Stevenson	1975	Daniel P. Moynihan	1992	Edward J. Perkins
1965	Arthur J. Goldberg	1976	William W. Scranton	1993	Madeleine K. Albright
1968	George W. Ball	1977	Andrew J. Young, Jr.	1997	Bill Richardson
1968	James R. Wiggins	1979	Donald F. McHenry	1999	Richard C. Holbrooke

DIRECTIONS: Interpreting a Chart Use the chart to answer the following questions.

1. Who served as United States representative to the United Nations in 1985?

_____

2. Who was the United States representative in 1972?

_____

3. Who was the representative to the United Nations in 1968?

_____

4. How many women have held the position? Who were they?

_____

5. Which representative served for the longest time period?

_____

Activity

DIRECTIONS: Making a Speech You are the United States representative to the United Nations. A new secretary general has taken office with promises to institute needed reforms in the United Nations. You have been asked to deliver an address expressing what reforms you think are most important for the world at this time. Deliver your speech to your classmates. Then ask for their feedback on your speech.

★ Enrichment Activity 27-2

Veto Means "I Forbid"

The veto power provides one of the checks and balances of power in the government of the United States. Democratic president Harry S Truman made use of the veto power to control the actions of the Republican Congress. The chart below shows how many times Truman and some other presidents have used the veto.

Some Presidential Vetoes

President	Years	Vetoes	Vetoes Overridden	President	Years	Vetoes	Vetoes Overridden
Washington	1789–97	2	0	Roosevelt, T.	1901–09	42	1
Madison	1809–17	5	0	Hoover	1929–33	21	3
Jackson	1829–37	5	0	Roosevelt, F. D.	1933–45	372	9
Lincoln	1861–65	2	0	Truman	1945–53	180	12
Johnson, A.	1865–69	21	15	Eisenhower	1953–61	73	2
Grant	1869–77	45	4	Kennedy	1961–63	12	0
Arthur	1881–85	4	1	Nixon	1969–74	26	7
Cleveland (first term)	1885–89	304	1	Reagan	1981–89	39	10
McKinley	1897–01	6	0	Bush, G.H.W.	1999–93	29	1

DIRECTIONS: Interpreting a Chart Use the chart to answer the following questions.

1. How many times did Truman veto bills? _____

2. Which president listed used the veto power most frequently? _____

3. How many times was Truman's veto overridden by Congress? _____

4. Which president's vetoes were most frequently overridden by Congress?

_____

5. In general did presidents of the 1800s or 1900s use the veto power more

frequently? _____

Activity **DIRECTIONS: Taking a Poll** The power to veto legislation is one of the checks and balances of our governmental system. Sometimes, however, the president and Congress reach a stalemate, as they did over the budget in 1996. How do most people feel about veto power? Conduct a poll to find out. Get as large a sample as possible. Ask some young people and some older people and compare their views.

★ Enrichment Activity 27-3

The War in Korea

The outline map to the right shows Korea.

DIRECTIONS: Follow the directions to complete the map.

1. Label the line that represents the 38th parallel.

2. Label North Korea and South Korea.

3. The Sea of Japan lies east of Korea, and the Yellow Sea lies to the west. Label these two bodies of water.

4. Locate and label Seoul, which lies south of the 38th parallel on a river that flows northwest into the sea.

5. Label the People's Republic of China, which lies to the north of Korea. Label the Yalu River, which forms part of the border with the People's Republic of China.

6. Label Pusan, which lies on the southeast tip of Korea.

7. Label Inchon, which lies southwest of Seoul on a tiny inlet on the coast.

8. Label Pyongyang, at the end of a deep bay on the western coast of North Korea.

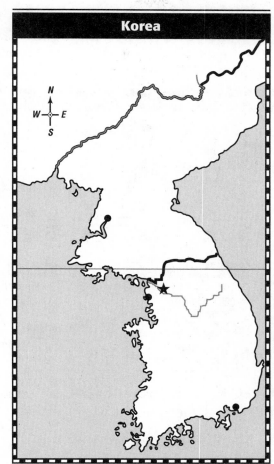

Korea

SECTION 27-3

Activity

DIRECTIONS: Creating A Scrapbook Since the Korean War, the Korean Peninsula has remained divided into North Korea and South Korea. Use the media center to find out more about the two Koreas. How are the cultures similar and different? How have the two countries developed economically and politically since the Korean War? Prepare a Korean travel scrapbook, using maps, pictures, and information to compare and contrast North Korea and South Korea.

★ Enrichment Activity 27-4

SECTION 27-4

Response to the Red Scare

Technology advanced during the years between 1945 and 1954. The Red Scare resulted in a rapid increase in the development of technologies that could be used for defense. Study the time line below.

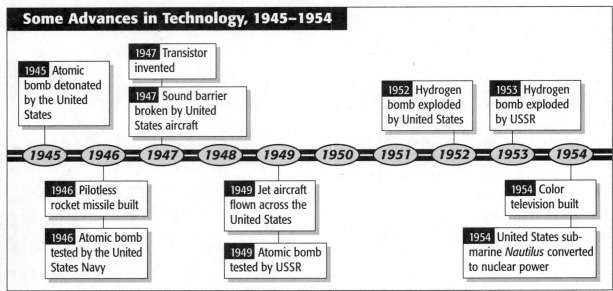

Some Advances in Technology, 1945–1954

1945 Atomic bomb detonated by the United States

1947 Transistor invented

1947 Sound barrier broken by United States aircraft

1952 Hydrogen bomb exploded by United States

1953 Hydrogen bomb exploded by USSR

1945 — 1946 — 1947 — 1948 — 1949 — 1950 — 1951 — 1952 — 1953 — 1954

1946 Pilotless rocket missile built

1946 Atomic bomb tested by the United States Navy

1949 Jet aircraft flown across the United States

1949 Atomic bomb tested by USSR

1954 Color television built

1954 United States submarine *Nautilus* converted to nuclear power

DIRECTIONS: Interpreting a Time Line Use the time line to answer the following questions.

1. In what year did the United States first explode an atomic bomb? _____

2. How many years passed before the Soviet Union exploded its first atomic bomb?

_____

3. What developments occurred in 1946? _____

_____

4. How many years passed between the explosion of a hydrogen bomb by the

United States and by the Soviet Union? _____

5. What happened in the same year that a United States aircraft reached supersonic

speeds? _____

Activity **DIRECTIONS: Writing a Memo** Which of the technological changes shown on the time line could have been used for defense? You are an FBI agent in charge of maintaining security on the technologies. Write a memo to the other agents in your office in which you explain how the technologies could be used and how you recommend that security be maintained.

Chapter 28 Resources

CHAPTER 28

★ **Vocabulary Activity 28**

DIRECTIONS: Word Cross Complete the puzzle by using the definitions to spell out each term. Then fill in the missing letters to write the term spelled vertically. Write the term and its definition on line 11.

summit	arms race	peaceful coexistence	moderate
surplus	affluence	standard of living	automation
domino theory	per capita income	productivity	

1. the average income of every individual in the nation
   1 _ _ _ _ _ | _ _ _ _ _ _ _ _

2. a measure of people's overall wealth and quality of life
   2 _ _ _ _ _ | _ _ _ _ _ _ _ _

3. middle-of-the-road
   3 _ _ _ _ | _ _ _

4. excess
   4 _ _ _ _ _ _ _

5. wealth
   5 _ _ _ _ _ _ _ | _

6. the belief that if one nation in Asia fell to the Communists, others would also fall
   6 _ _ _ _ _ _ | _ _ _

7. a meeting of heads of government
   7 _ _ _ | _ _

8. the ability to produce more goods
   8 _ _ _ _ _ _ _ _ | _

9. _ _ _ _ _ _ | _ _

10. producing goods using mechanical and electronic devices
    10 _ _ _ _ _ _ | _ _

11. _____

_____

10. the building up of more and more weapons by two (or more) nations in an effort to surpass the other's military strength

DIRECTIONS: Using Vocabulary Use each of the following terms correctly in a complete sentence. Write the sentences on a separate sheet of paper.

baby boom	ghetto	materialism

★ **Chapter Skills Activity 28**

Analyzing Information

Information can be presented in many forms, such as a chart, a paragraph, a photo, or a song. Being able to analyze this information will allow you to have a better understanding of its meaning. As you review the information below, look at how it is organized and identify the topic.

United States Foreign Aid, 1945–1961

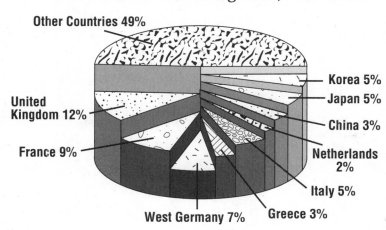

DIRECTIONS: Answer the questions on a separate sheet of paper.

1. What does this graph show?

_____

2. What was the total percentage of United States foreign aid given to the

United Kingdom? _____

3. What total percentage of foreign aid was given to Korea, Japan, and China?

_____

CRITICAL THINKING

4. **Identifying Central Issues** What is the main topic of the graphic above? How do you know this?

Activity   **DIRECTIONS:** Listen to a song with lyrics and try to analyze the information presented. Think about the meaning that the singer or songwriter is trying to communicate. On a separate sheet of paper, summarize the song's meaning in your own words.

CHAPTER 28

Critical Thinking Skills Activity 28 | Analyzing Information

SOCIAL STUDIES OBJECTIVE: Analyze information by distinguishing between fact and nonfact

LEARNING THE SKILL

A fact is a statement that can be proven. An opinion is a personal belief that cannot be proven.

Read the following example.

Fact: Project Mercury was the first American program to send astronauts into space.

Opinion: The money spent on Project Mercury should have been spent on education and health care.

To distinguish facts and opinions as you read a book, newspaper, or magazine article, check for statements that you can verify. Statements that use "should," "the most important," "the best," or "the most interesting" are often opinion.

APPLYING THE SKILL

DIRECTIONS: Read the following passage. Then identify each numbered sentence by writing **F** if it is a fact or **O** if it is an opinion. Give a reason for each choice.

The Cold War

(1) The United States and the Soviet Union did not actually fight a war during the 1950s. (2) The two nations, however, were still bitter rivals. (3) Everyone knew the United States was a better nation. (4) However, the United States still feared the spread of communism, along with possible attacks against other nations by the Soviets. (5) President Eisenhower proposed a policy of massive retaliation—an instant nuclear attack—if the Soviets dared to attack other nations. (6) Critics called this policy "brinksmanship." (7) Eisenhower was never tempted to put this policy into effect. (8) If Eisenhower had used the American military to attack the Soviet Union, the Soviet Union would have definitely lost.

1. _____

_____

_____

2. _____

_____

_____

3. _____

_____

_____

CHAPTER 28

Critical Thinking Skills Activity 28 | Analyzing Information

---

4. _____

_____

_____

5. _____

_____

_____

6. _____

_____

_____

7. _____

_____

_____

8. _____

_____

_____

PRACTICING THE SKILLS

DIRECTIONS: In the blank at the left, write the letter of the choice that best answers the question.

_____ **1.** Which of following statements is a fact?
   A. The United States was destined to win the space race.
   B. Soviet people had more desire to improve their country than Americans did in the 1950s.
   C. The Soviet Union launched *Sputnik,* the first satellite.
   D. The United States should have sent the first satellite into orbit.

_____ **2.** Which of the following statements is an opinion?
   A. The Cold War was a necessary conflict between two great military powers.
   B. In the early 1950s, French soldiers fought in Vietnam.
   C. Nikita Khrushchev became the Soviet leader after the death of Stalin.
   D. Eisenhower believed that if one nation in Asia fell to communism, others would fall as well.

Name _____ Date _____ Class _____

★ GEOGRAPHY AND HISTORY ACTIVITY 28

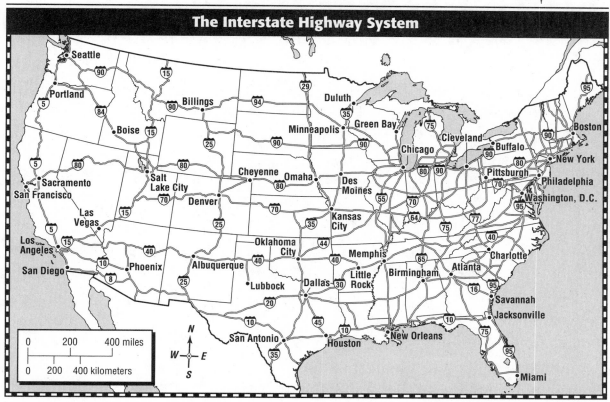

The Interstate Highway System

DIRECTIONS: Write your answers to questions 1–4 on the map. You may abbreviate if you wish.

1. Trace in blue the shortest interstate highway route from New York City to Miami.

2. Circle the numbers of the interstate highways you would take on a trip from Portland, Oregon, to Denver, Colorado. Then trace the route in red.

3. On a spring break, your class will take a bus to visit the nation's capital. Use green to trace the shortest interstate highway route the bus would take from your home state to Washington, D.C.

4. Circle the names of the cities at the eastern and western ends of Interstate 10.

5. Study the map. Then explain the system you think was used to number the

   interstate highways. _____

   _____

   _____

   _____

★ **Time Line Activity 28**

Arab-Israeli Relations

DIRECTIONS: Read the following background information. Then examine the time line. Use what you learn to answer the questions in the spaces provided.

ARAB-ISRAELI CONFLICTS/WARS

1956 Israel seizes Gaza Strip and most of Sinai Peninsula in Suez-Sinai War

1967 Six-Day War is waged between Arabs and Israelis

1973 Arab states attack Israel during Yom Kippur War

1991 Israel refrains from direct involvement in Persian Gulf War

1947 UN partitions Palestine into two states

1948 Israel declares its independence

1979 Egypt signs peace treaty with Israel

1993 Israel and PLO reach agreement on Palestinian self-rule

1994 Israel and Jordan formally end their state of war

2000 Israel ends its 18-year occupation of Lebanon

(Time line years: 1940, 1950, 1960, 1970, 1980, 1990, 2000)

POLITICAL EVENTS

CRISIS IN THE MIDDLE EAST

▣ Background

Tensions in the Middle East developed when the Arab states rejected the existence of the modern state of Israel in 1948. Through the years conflicts erupted into several major wars in the area. From the late 1970s to the present, peace negotiations between Israel and individual Arab nations have met with varying levels of success.

1. From what country did Israel withdraw its forces in 2000?

2. How many days did the brief 1967 war between Arabs and Israelis last?

3. In what year did Egypt and Israel sign a peace treaty?

4. On what basic issue did Israel and the PLO reach agreement in 1993?

5. In which war did Israel *not* become directly involved?

6. During which war did Israel seize the Gaza Strip?

7. When did Israel and Jordan formally end their state of war?

CHAPTER 28

Name _____ Date _____ Class _____

Linking Past and Present Activity 28

Space Exploration

THEN The space age began on October 4, 1957, when the Soviet Union launched a 29-inch satellite called *Sputnik I.* It was the first object to be sent beyond Earth's atmosphere.

Sputnik I profoundly affected Americans. It signaled the beginning of the "space race"—an ongoing competition between the United States and the Soviet Union to explore space. The space race was an outgrowth of the Cold War between the two nations.

On January 31, 1958, the United States launched its first satellite, *Explorer I.* Then on April 12, 1961, Soviet cosmonaut Yuri Gagarin  became the first human to fly beyond Earth's atmosphere into space. Less than a month later, on May 5, 1961, Alan B. Shepard, Jr., became the first American in space.

NOW Today Russian and American scientists explore space together. In July 1975 a historic "handshake in space" began joint scientific endeavors. The United States *Apollo* capsule docked with the Soviet *Soyuz* spacecraft, creating a temporary space station.

In 1986 the Soviet Union boosted into orbit the first permanently-manned orbiting space station. They named it *Mir,* which means "peace." American astronauts, including Norman Thagard, Shannon Lucid, and John Blaha, have lived aboard *Mir* with Russian cosmonauts.

The first crew of one American and two Russians arrived at the International Space Station on November 2, 2000. The station is being built in space by astronauts and scientists from the United States, Russia, Canada, Japan, and the European Space Agency. The United States *Space Shuttle* and Russian *Soyuz* spacecraft will carry new modules, crews, and supplies to the station.

CHAPTER 28

Activity

DIRECTIONS: Completing a Chart The chart below lists five notable space flights. Research to find out what year each flight took place and why it was important. Then complete the chart.

Space Voyages			
Spacecraft Name	**Mission Commander(s)**	**Year**	**Mission Description**
1. *Vostok I*	Yuri Gagarin		
2. *Friendship 7*	John Glenn		
3. *Vostok VI*	Valentina Tereshkova		
4. *Apollo 11*	Neil Armstrong, Buzz Aldrin, Michael Collins		
5. *Columbia* (maiden voyage)	Robert Crippen, John Young		

★ Primary Source Reading 28

Rock 'n Roll Arrives

> ⊠ **Interpreting the Source** This magazine article, titled "A Question of Questionable Meanings," appeared in 1955. As you read about the new music craze, think about why it alarmed many adults.

The heavy-beat and honking-melody tunes of today's rock 'n roll have a clearly defined ancestry in U.S. jazz going back to Louis Armstrong and Bessie Smith of 30 years ago. Once called "race" records, and later "rhythm and blues," the music was first performed by [African Americans] and sold mostly in [African American] communities. During the past years as the big record companies concentrated on mambos and ballads, the country's teen-agers found themselves without snappy dance tunes to their taste. A few disk jockies filled the void with songs like *Ko Ko Mo, Tweedlee Dee, Hearts of Stone, Earth Angel, Flip, Flop, and Fly, Shake, Rattle and Roll*, and the name rock 'n roll took over. On a list of 10 top juke box best-selling records last week, six were r 'n r.

But parents and police were startled by other rock 'n roll records' words, which were frequently suggestive and occasionally lewd. *Variety*, the show business weekly, cranked out indignant [angry] stories about "leerics" in the rock 'n roll or rhythm and blues songs. *Cash Box*, the juke box trade journal, countered that much of the suggestiveness was read into the songs by low-minded listeners and challenged anybody to find smut in the top rock 'n roll numbers.

By this time, however, the music had gained such an exaggerated reputation that the worst meanings could be found in the most innocent phrases. Radio, TV and record censors listened not only to rock 'n roll but also— with good reason—to the lyrics of pop records. But hardly a teen-ager afoot had time to listen. They all seemed to be busily and blithely [carelessly] rockin' and rollin' around.

SOURCE: *Life* magazine, April 18, 1955, page 168.

DOCUMENT-BASED QUESTION

DIRECTIONS: Answer the following question on a separate sheet of paper. Compare the two opinions about rock 'n roll that are mentioned in this article.

DIRECTIONS: Media Literacy Look in current periodicals for discussions of adults' concerns about music preferred by teenagers today. Clip or copy at least two articles. Combine them with your written response to this question: Why does music stir up controversy?

Chapter 28 Section Resources

★ Guided Reading Activity 28-1

DIRECTIONS: Filling in the Blanks Use your textbook to fill in the blanks using the words in the box. Use another sheet of paper if necessary.

supreme commander	December 1957	Soviet Union	*Sputnik*
peaceful coexistence	Middle East	Republican	moderate
private enterprise	Budapest, Hungary	NATO	Cold War
John J. Sparkman	"Spirit of Geneva"	Richard M. Nixon	Korea
Dwight D. Eisenhower	Adlai E. Stevenson		

Republican Revival

In the 1952 presidential election, the Democrats nominated **(1)** _____ for president and Senator **(2)** _____ of Alabama as his running mate. The Republicans chose General **(3)** _____ for president and **(4)** _____, a senator from California, for vice president. Eisenhower rose through the army to become **(5)** _____ of the Allied forces in Europe during World War II. Eisenhower won wide support with his pledge to end the war in **(6)** _____. Eisenhower was the first **(7)** _____ to win the White House since 1928.

Domestic Policy

During his two terms in office, Eisenhower followed a **(8)** _____ approach to domestic policy. Eisenhower supported economic policies aimed at limiting government spending and encouraging **(9)** _____.

Eisenhower and the Cold War

In **(10)** _____ the United States attempted to launch its own space satellite after the Soviet Union had successfully sent **(11)** _____, the world's first artificial satellite, into space. This rivalry kept the **(12)** _____ at the center of American foreign policy.

Foreign Policy Challenges

Fighting broke out in the **(13)** _____ in 1956. In October of that year, demonstrators in **(14)** _____ called for changes in their government. The United States and the **(15)** _____ were on opposing sides with both incidents. Finally, Eisenhower, **(16)** _____ leaders, and Soviet officials met to discuss disarmament and German reunification. The **(17)** _____ renewed hopes for peace, but the new policy of **(18)** _____ ended in 1960.

★ Guided Reading Activity 28-2

DIRECTIONS: Recalling the Facts Use the information in your textbook to answer the questions. Use another sheet of paper if necessary.

1. What contributed to economic growth in the United States from 1945 to 1960?

   _____

2. What were early computers like? _____

3. What company led the field in the sales of computers by 1955? _____

4. How much did per capita income increase in the United States between 1945

   and 1960? _____

5. What changes transformed Americans' social and cultural life? _____

6. What was the soaring birthrate of the postwar years called? _____

7. Where did 85 percent of new home construction take place during the 1950s?

   _____

8. Who introduced mass-produced housing? _____

9. What was the name of the community on Long Island, New York, that included

   more than 17,000 identical houses? _____

10. Who were generally denied the opportunities of the postwar suburbs? _____

11. On what did life in suburban America center? _____

12. What was the drive-in capital of the nation? _____

13. What helped create consumer fads and crazes that swept the nation in the 1950s?

   _____

14. What profoundly changed American life?

   _____

15. What form of music achieved great popularity in the 1950s? _____

16. What did the differing attitudes of the older and younger generations toward

   music, as well as other forms of culture, come to be called? _____

Copyright © by The McGraw-Hill Companies, Inc.

★ Guided Reading Activity 28-3

DIRECTIONS: Filling in the Blanks Fill in the blanks using the words in the box. Use another sheet of paper if necessary.

African American sharecroppers	**factories**	**three million**	**beatniks**
John Kenneth Galbraith	**coal industry**	**civil rights**	**ghettos**
suburban housewives	**Betty Friedan**	**Appalachia**	**Hispanics**
business enterprises	**synthetic fibers**	**urban areas**	**the Beats**

Poverty

Large **(1)** _____ bought vast areas of available farmland. Many small farm families sold their farms and migrated to **(2)** _____. Those who stayed often struggled to stay out of poverty. In the South the problems of **(3)** _____ and tenant farmers increased when mechanized cotton pickers replaced workers. The popularity of **(4)** _____ reduced the demand for cotton, causing Southern farmworkers to lose their jobs and farmers to lose their land. The decline of the **(5)** _____ in **(6)** _____ plunged thousands of rural mountain people into poverty. Between 1940 and 1960, more than **(7)** _____ African Americans from the South moved to cities in the North and the Midwest. Many poor **(8)** _____ also moved to cities. The "white flight" that followed turned some areas of cities into **(9)** _____. As whites fled the cities, **(10)** _____ and businesses also relocated to suburban areas, reducing the number of job opportunities for the urban poor.

Voices of Dissent

In *The Affluent Society*, **(11)** _____ claimed that suburban families often ignored the problems and hardships faced by other Americans. A group of writers called **(12)** _____ sharply criticized American society. The millions of young Americans who read their works and adopted their attitudes and ideas were called **(13)** _____. In her book, *The Feminine Mystique*, **(14)** _____ described the frustration and unhappiness of **(15)** _____ dissatisfied with their image. African Americans became less willing to accept their status as second-class citizens and launched a new campaign for full **(16)** _____.

★ **Reteaching Activity 28-1**

DIRECTIONS: Organizing Facts Follow the directions in the chart to create a profile of Dwight D. Eisenhower and his presidency.

Dwight D. Eisenhower

I. Fill in the information for each of these items related to Eisenhower.

Education	
Military Experience	
Nickname	
Political Party	
Vice President	
Election Opponent	

II. Put a check mark next to Eisenhower's policies, beliefs, and actions.

A. Followed a moderate approach to domestic policy	
B. Avoided ambitious new government programs	
C. Abolished popular old programs	
D. Wanted to make the federal government bigger	
E. Removed wage and price controls	
F. Believed the government should protect the basic welfare of Americans	
G. Made drastic changes in Social Security and other New Deal programs to reduce their effectiveness	
H. Believed in the domino theory	

III. Answer the following questions about major events and accomplishments of the Eisenhower administration.

A. The Department of Health, Education, and Welfare (1953)

    1. Who was its first secretary?

B. The Federal Highway Act (1956)

    1. Why did Congress pass this act?

    2. What did this law fund?

C. New States

    1. What states entered the Union and in what year?

D. The Arms Race

    1. What two superpowers competed to surpass each other's military strength?

SECTION 28-1

★ **Reteaching Activity 28-2**

DIRECTIONS: Determining Cause and Effect Complete the top part of the diagram by writing the letters from the Fact Bank of the contributing factors to the prosperity and growth of the 1950s. In the bottom part of the diagram, write the letters of items that further explain the effects of prosperity and growth on the nation.

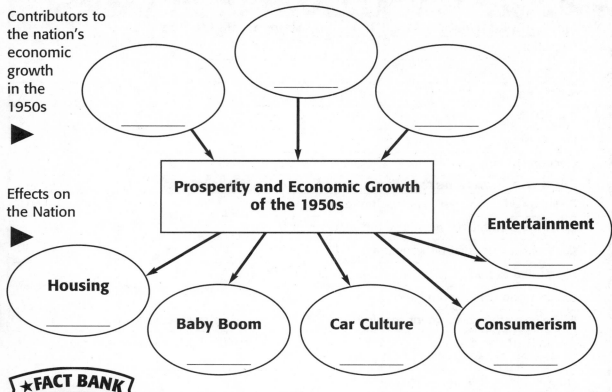

Contributors to the nation's economic growth in the 1950s ▶

Effects on the Nation ▶

Prosperity and Economic Growth of the 1950s

Entertainment

Housing

Baby Boom

Car Culture

Consumerism

★**FACT BANK**

A. The focus of society shifted to children and their needs.

B. People ate fast food and went to the movies without leaving their cars.

C. Business and industry invested in new technology, such as computers.

D. Eighty-five percent of new homes were built in the suburbs.

E. Rock 'n' roll swept the nation, as performers such as Chuck Berry and Elvis Presley became popular.

F. The military spent a large amount of money for the Korean War.

G. People used credit to buy goods.

H. In the suburbs people needed cars to get to work and to shop.

I. Millions of Americans watched television programs such as *I Love Lucy*.

J. The nation's population increased by about 20 percent.

K. Government increased spending on social programs.

L. Advertising created fads and a demand for specific products.

M. William Levitt introduced methods for rapid construction of homes.

SECTION 28-2

★ **Reteaching Activity 28-3**

DIRECTIONS: Crossword Puzzle Complete the crossword puzzle about poverty and the changing values of society in the 1950s.

On the Road	**Little Rock**	**Appalachia**	**synthetics**
Betty Friedan	**materialism**	**Montgomery**	**ghetto**
automation	**white flight**	*The Affluent Society*	**beatniks**

Across

1. focus on accumulating money and possessions

3. book by economist John Kenneth Galbraith

4. novel by Beat author Jack Kerouac

9. neighborhood inhabited mainly by poor minority group

10. the rapid departure of middle-class white Americans to the suburbs

11. producing goods using mechanical and electronic devices

Down

1. African Americans staged a successful bus boycott here

2. adopted attitudes of rebellion and isolation from society

5. decline of the coal industry plunged thousands into poverty here

6. described the frustration and unhappiness of suburban housewives

7. federal troops helped enforce an order to integrate a high school here

8. their popularity reduced the demand for cotton

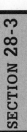

SECTION 28-3

★ Enrichment Activity 28-1

Names of States

State names have many different origins that reflect the variety of people and cultures that make up the United States.

DIRECTIONS: Using Context Clues Match each origin of a state name with one of the state names in the box.

Georgia	Nevada	Tennessee	Indiana	Louisiana
Pennsylvania	Arizona	Alaska	Hawaii	Michigan

1. _____ After a Cherokee village called *tanasi*

2. _____ From its people's native word *hawaiki* or *owhyhee*, which means "homeland"

3. _____ From an Aztec word, *arizuma,* which means "having silver"

4. _____ For King George II of England, who granted a charter for the founding of the colony

5. _____ Adopted by the Russians from an Aleutian word *alakshak,* or "land that is not an island"

6. _____ From a Chippewa word *micigama*, meaning "great water"

7. _____ For the French King Louis XIV

8. _____ After the colony's founder, William Penn

9. _____ Coined by English-speaking settlers to mean "land of the Indians"

10. _____ From a Spanish word that means "snow-clad"

Activity

DIRECTIONS: Creating a Brochure How did your state, county, or city get its name? Use the media center, a local historical society, or the Internet to find information. Create a brochure in which you mention the history of the name, the attractions of the location, and a map or drawings and photographs of the place.

SECTION 28-1

★ Enrichment Activity 28-2

Centers of Population

One way to look at population changes is to consider the center of population of a country. Suppose the United States with all its people makes up a huge flat plate. The center of population is the point at which this flat-plate country would balance on a point placed underneath it.

Activity **DIRECTIONS:** Use the information below to plot the changing centers of population of the United States. On the map make a color-coded dot and write the date to show the location of the center of population for each given year.

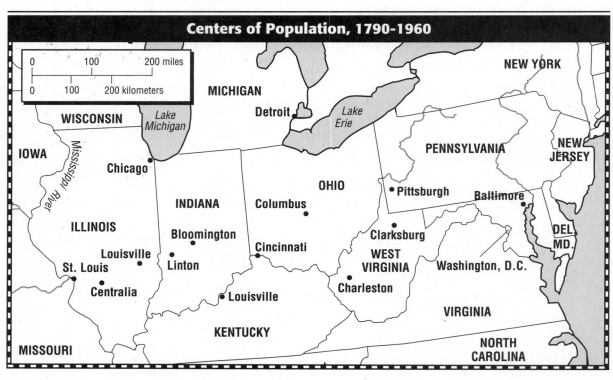

Centers of Population, 1790-1960

1. 1790; red; about 25 miles east of Baltimore, Maryland

2. 1800; orange; about 20 miles west of Baltimore, Maryland

3. 1840; yellow; about 15 miles south of Clarksburg, West Virginia

4. 1870; green; about 48 miles northeast of Cincinnati, Ohio

5. 1910; blue; in Bloomington, Indiana

6. 1930; purple; about 3 miles northeast of Linton, Indiana

7. 1950; brown; about 3 miles northeast of Louisville, Illinois

8. 1960; black; about 7 miles northwest of Centralia, Illinois

★ Enrichment Activity 28-3 ★  ★

Plane Wreck at Los Gatos

Migrant workers were among the people who did not share in the prosperity of the 1950s. The folk song excerpted below, with words by Woody Guthrie, describes the plight of a group of migrant workers from Mexico whose plane crashed on their return trip home.

Copyright © by The McGraw-Hill Companies, Inc.

Plane Wreck at Los Gatos

The crops are all in and the peaches are rott'ning,
The oranges piled in their creosote dumps;
You're flying 'em back to the Mexican border
To pay all their money to wade back again.

CHORUS: Goodbye to my Juan, goodbye Rosalita;
           Adios mis amigos, Jesus y Maria,
           You won't have your names when you ride the big airplane,
           All they will call you will be deportees.

The sky plane caught fire over Los Gatos Canyon,
A fireball of lightning it shook all our hills.
Who are all these friends all scattered like dry leaves?
The radio says they are just deportees.

Is this the best way we can grow our big orchards?
Is this the best way we can grow our good fruit?
To fall like dry leaves to rot on my top soil
And be called by no name except deportees?

SOURCE: PLANE WRECK AT LOS GATOS (Deportee) Words by Woody Guthrie; Music by Martin Hoffman
TRO-©-Copyright 1961 (Renewed) 1963 (Renewed) Ludlow Music, Inc., New York, New York Used by
Permission.

SECTION 28-3

Activity

DIRECTIONS: Writing a Radio Script Rewrite the radio broadcast that announced the plane crash described in the song. Prepare a radio script, including interviews at the site and your narrative of events. If possible, have classmates take the roles of interviewees and record your radio broadcast.

Chapter 29 Resources

★ Vocabulary Activity 29

DIRECTIONS: Identifying Related and Unrelated Terms Write terms from the list below that fit each description.

| Medicaid | sit-in | integrate | civil disobedience |
| Medicare | boycott | segregation | |

1. Two related terms: one means the separation of people of different races; the other means to bring people of different races together.

_____

2. Three related terms: one refers to protest methods based on the refusal to obey laws that are considered unjust; the second is a type of protest in which people refuse to use a service or a product; the third is the act of protesting by sitting down in one place and refusing to move.

_____

3. Two related terms: the first is a program established during the Johnson administration that helped pay for medical care for senior citizens; the second is a program also established during the Johnson administration that helped poor people pay their hospital bills.

_____

DIRECTIONS: Understanding Definitions Select the term that answers each question below. Write the correct term in the space provided.

| Hispanic | interstate | feminist | poverty line |

4. What word refers to the minimum income needed to survive? _____

_____

5. What word means across state lines? _____

6. What word names an American who came, or whose ancestors came, to the United States from the countries of Latin America or Spain? _____

_____

7. What word refers to activists for women's rights? _____

CHAPTER 29

★ **Chapter Skills Activity 29**

Drawing Conclusions

Whether you are reading a newspaper article or a science fiction story, you may need to read "between the lines" to understand the author's meaning. Authors do not always state their meaning directly. By considering the facts presented and using your own knowledge and insight, you can draw conclusions about an author's meaning.

DIRECTIONS: Filling in the Blanks The excerpt below is from a speech that Malcolm X made in Detroit in 1965. Read the excerpt and answer the questions below.

> "Now, what effect does [the struggle over Africa] have on us? Why should the black man in America concern himself since he's been away from the African continent for three or four hundred years? Why should we concern ourselves? What impact does what happens have upon us? Number one, you have to realize that up until 1959 Africa was dominated by the colonial powers. Having complete control over Africa, the colonial powers of Europe projected the image of Africa negatively . . . it was so negative that it was negative to you and me, and you and I began to hate it. We didn't want anybody telling us anything about Africa, much less calling us Africans. In hating Africa and in hating the Africans, we ended up hating ourselves, without even realizing it. Because you can't hate the roots of a tree, and not hate the tree. You can't hate your origin and not end up hating yourself. You can't hate Africa and not hate yourself."

1. What struggle in Africa was Malcolm X referring to in the first sentence? _____

_____

2. According to Malcolm X, why did many African Americans have a negative image

of themselves? _____

_____

3. Did Malcolm X believe that events in Africa should concern African Americans in

the United States? Why or why not? _____

_____

4. Why do you think Malcolm X believed that a more positive image of Africa was

needed to empower African Americans to fight for civil rights? _____

_____

_____

Critical Thinking Skills Activity 29 | Drawing Conclusions

SOCIAL STUDIES OBJECTIVE: Analyze information by drawing conclusions

LEARNING THE SKILL

When you read a book or an article, you may need to add knowledge you already have to understand its meaning fully. By considering the facts presented and using your own knowledge, you can draw conclusions that allow you to go beyond what is actually stated on the page.

> We used to [start] work . . . about four o'clock in the morning. We'd pick the harvest until about six. Then we'd . . . [go] to school . . . By the time we got to school, we'd be all tuckered out. Around maybe eleven o'clock, we'd be dozing off. Our teachers would send notes to the house saying we were inattentive. . . . Many times we never did our homework, because we were out in the fields . . .
>
> School would end maybe four o'clock. We'd rush home [and] . . . go back to work until seven. . . . On Saturday and Sunday, we'd be . . . [in the fields] from four thirty in the morning until about seven thirty in the evening. . . .
>
> If we had proper compensation we wouldn't have to working seventeen hours a day and following the crops. We could stay in one area and it would give us roots. Being a migrant . . . tears the family apart. . . . The children are the ones hurt the most. They go to school three months in one place and then on to another. No sooner do they make friends, they are uprooted again. . . .
>
> If people could see—in the winter . . . ice on fields . . . We'd be [working] on our knees all day long. . . . We'd be picking watermelons [in the summer] in 105 degrees all day long. When people have melons or cucumbers or carrots or lettuce, they don't know how they got on the table and the consequences to the people who picked it. . . .
>
> —From an interview of Roberto Acuna, who was a migrant farm laborer as a child and young adult during the 1950s and 1960s.

SOURCE: Terkel, Studs, *Working.* New York: Avon Books, 1975, pp. 30–38.

APPLYING THE SKILL

DIRECTIONS: Answer the questions using the passage.

1. How did migrant farmwork affect the education of children?

_____

_____

_____

2. Does Roberto Acuna think children should have been migrant farm-workers? Explain your answer.

_____

_____

_____

(continued)

Critical Thinking Skills Activity 29 | Drawing Conclusions

3. How does Roberto Acuna think a raise in pay would have affected the families of migrant farmworkers?

_____

_____

_____

4. Does Roberto Acuna think that the general public knew about the conditions of migrant farmworkers? Did he think they should have known? Why?

_____

_____

_____

PRACTICING THE SKILL

DIRECTIONS: In the blank at the left, write the letter of the choice that best answers the question.

_____ **1.** Which of the following should you read, in addition to the views of Roberto Acuna, to have more knowledge about the conditions of migrant farmworkers in the 1950s and 1960s?
   A. Read the views of a farmer who employs migrant farmworkers and the views of companies that buy the crops that the farmworkers pick.
   B. Read the views of a farmer who employs migrant farmworkers and a government report on these farmworkers in America.
   C. Read the biographies of the parents of Roberto Acuna and a magazine article on immigration.
   D. Reading the passage above is enough.

_____ **2.** Did Roberto Acuna's teachers understand the type of life he lived away from school?
   A. Yes, his teachers offered to give him extra help when he had to work long hours.
   B. Yes, because Roberto Acuna told his teachers about his life.
   C. No, his teachers did not understand why he was tired in class.
   D. No, because his teachers had no interest in him.

_____ **3.** What conclusion can you make about why children worked in the fields?
   A. The children enjoyed working in the fields.
   B. Children of migrant farmworkers were required to work with their parents by law.
   C. The children preferred working in the fields to attending school.
   D. The children worked in the fields because their families probably needed the money they earned.

Name _____ Date _____ Class _____

DIRECTIONS: Write your answers to questions 1–4 on the map. You may abbreviate if you wish.

1. As a result of the Voting Rights Act of 1965, the number of African Americans who registered to vote increased markedly in the South. Examine the maps. Then use red to color the state (on the 1966 map) where the percentage of registered African American voters showed the greatest increase between 1960 and 1966.

2. Use blue to color the state (on the 1966 map) that made the smallest gain in African American voter registration.

3. Use green to color the state (on the 1966 map) that had the highest percentage of African American voter registration in both 1960 and 1966.

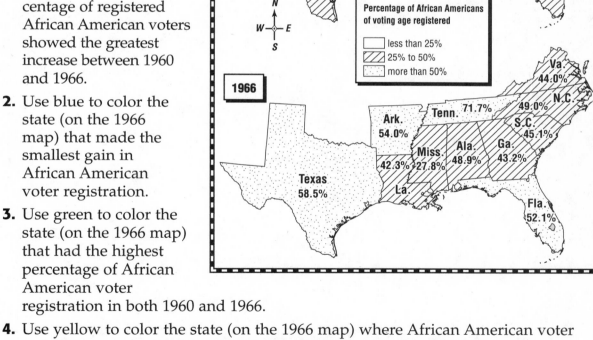

African American Voter Registration in the South, 1960 and 1966

4. Use yellow to color the state (on the 1966 map) where African American voter registration was more than five times greater in 1966 than in 1960.

5. Do you think the Voting Rights Act achieved its objective? Use information from

these maps to help explain your answer. _____

_____

_____

★ **Time Line Activity 29**

United States Civil and Human Rights

DIRECTIONS: Use the following information to make a time line about United States civil rights acts and international human rights developments. Include the date for each event.

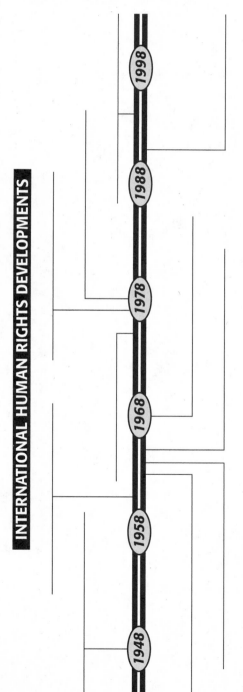

INTERNATIONAL HUMAN RIGHTS DEVELOPMENTS

1998

1988

1978

1968

1958

1948

INTERNATIONAL HUMAN RIGHTS DEVELOPMENTS

☒ **Background**

International standards on human rights were set in a series of declarations and agreements following World War II. The United Nations (UN) Declaration of Human Rights was adopted by the UN General Assembly in 1948. In 1961 Amnesty International was launched to aid political and religious prisoners. This nongovernmental organization was awarded the Nobel Peace Prize in 1977. The United States, USSR, Canada, and the 32 European nations that signed the Helsinki Accords in 1975 pledged, among other things, to respect human rights. In 1978 the American Convention on Human Rights was set forth. In 1994 the UN General Assembly recommitted its efforts to the spirit of human rights by creating the UN Commission on Human Rights.

UNITED STATES CIVIL RIGHTS ACTS

- The Equal Pay Act of 1963 guarantees women equal pay (to men) for equal work.
- The Civil Rights Act of 1964 outlaws job discrimination.
- The Voting Rights Act of 1965 allows African Americans to register to vote.
- The Civil Rights Act of 1968 prohibits discrimination in housing and real estate.
- The Civil Rights Act of 1991 eases burden on workers suing to prove job discrimination.

CHAPTER 29

Linking Past and Present Activity 29

Marches on Washington, D.C.

 Protest marches and demonstrations were memorable features of the political movements that swept the 1960s and 1970s. Americans from many socioeconomic, ethnic, and age groups wanted their political voices to be heard. Many chose to join mass movements that gathered in Washington, D.C., where legislators and the president could see their strength in numbers. The goal was to affect political change.

The Civil Rights march on Washington in 1963 of more than 200,000 people sparked a wave of marches that continued into the next decade. Citizens marched to protest the war in Vietnam, to support women's rights, and to save the environment. New legislation and changes in public policy that addressed these concerns is due in part to this show of support from demonstrators.

 Marches on Washington continue to draw large numbers of supporters. In 1983 the twentieth anniversary of the Civil Rights march drew more people than the original event. As in the 1963 march, speakers reiterated themes from Martin Luther King, Jr.'s, "I Have a Dream" speech, and the crowd joined in singing "We Shall Overcome."

In October 1995 African American men gathered in the capital for the Million Man March. While the march fell short of 1 million participants, more than 400,000 mostly African American men attended. Civil rights leaders the Reverend Jesse Jackson, Rosa Parks, the Reverend Benjamin Chavis, and Betty Shabazz urged marchers to end the cycle of violence, drugs, and unemployment that holds back many impoverished communities.

CHAPTER 29

Activity

DIRECTIONS: Researching Historical Data Listed below are some of the marches held in Washington, D.C. Research each of these events and list the date of the event, the approximate number of people who attended, and one interesting fact about the event.

Marches on Washington, D.C.			
Event	**Date**	**Number of Marchers**	**Event Fact**
Vietnam War moratorium rally			
Vietnam War "Out Now" rally			
Return of hostages from Iran			
20th anniversary of Civil Rights march			
March for Women's Lives			

★ Primary Source Reading 29

Song of the Civil Rights Era

> ✖ **Interpreting the Source** Those who fought to end segregation used marches, sit-ins, boycotts, and songs. As you read the freedom song below, imagine the spirit with which it was sung in 1963.

If You Miss Me From the Back of the Bus

Words: Carver Neblett Music: Traditional
© 1963 (renewed) by Sanga Music Inc. All Rights Reserved. Used by Permission.

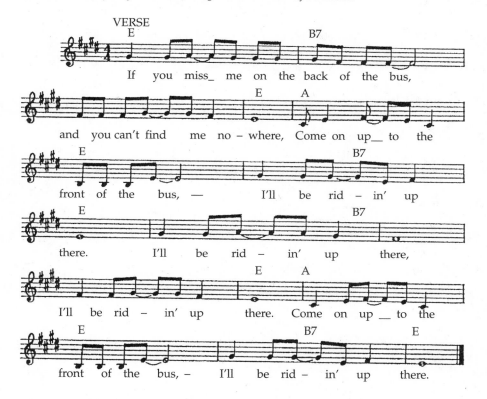

SOURCE: *Sing for Freedom: The Story of the Civil Rights Movement Through Its Songs,* compiled and edited by Guy and Candie Carawan. Bethlehem, PA: Sing Out Corporation, 1990.

DOCUMENT-BASED QUESTIONS

DIRECTIONS: Answer the following question on a separate sheet of paper.

1. Another verse of this song is "If you miss me from the front of the bus, and you can't find me nowhere,/Come on up to the driver's seat, I'll be drivin' up there." What does that verse mean?

2. The Montgomery bus boycott in 1956 is considered the start of the modern civil rights movement. Why do people use boycotts? When are boycotts most effective?

DIRECTIONS: Writing a Song Consider the state of civil rights and racial equality today. Write the lyrics to your own song expressing the fight for civil rights today.

Chapter 29 Section Resources

SECTIONS

★ Guided Reading Activity 29-1

DIRECTIONS: Outlining Locate the heading in your textbook. Then use the information under the heading to help you write each answer.

I. Equality in Education

  A. Introduction

    1. What organization, founded in 1909, attacked segregation in the 1950s?

    _____

    2. Who was the lawyer who decided to challenge the idea of "separate

    but equal"? _____

  B. The *Brown* Decision—What was the ruling of the Supreme Court in *Brown* v. *Board of Education of Topeka, Kansas*?

  _____

  C. Integrating the Schools—What were school authorities called on to do in the

  Court's decision in *Brown* v. *Board of Education of Topeka, Kansas*? _____

  _____

  D. Confrontation in Little Rock

    1. In 1957 who called out the National Guard to prevent African Americans

    from entering an all-white high school? _____

    2. How did President Dwight D. Eisenhower settle the problem? _____

II. Gains on Other Fronts

  A. The Montgomery Bus Boycott

    1. In 1955 what African American woman refused to move to the back of the

    bus in Montgomery, Alabama? _____

    2. What did this woman's refusal to move to the back of the bus cause?

    _____

  B. Nonviolent Protest

    1. Whose tactics did Martin Luther King, Jr., follow? _____

    2. What nonviolent protester from India also influenced King? _____

    3. What new organization did King and 60 other ministers start in January, 1957?

    _____

SECTION 29-1

★ **Guided Reading Activity 29-2**

DIRECTIONS: Recalling the Facts Use the information in your textbook to answer the questions. Use another sheet of paper if necessary.

1. Why did Richard M. Nixon lead John F. Kennedy in the polls for much of the 1960 presidential campaign? _____

2. What did Robert Donovan's book *PT 109* describe? _____

3. When and where did Kennedy's political career begin? _____

4. What was the turning point in the 1960 election? _____

5. What did Kennedy call his plan for the country? _____

6. What did the proposals in this plan involve? _____

7. What type of bill did Kennedy ask Congress to pass in 1963? _____

8. When and where was Kennedy assassinated? _____

9. Whom did police charge with Kennedy's assassination? What happened to that person? _____

10. What study concluded that the assassin had acted alone? _____

11. What did President Lyndon B. Johnson call the set of programs he presented soon after becoming president? _____

12. Name these programs designed to help poor Americans:

   a) provided preschool education for children of the poor _____

   b) helped poor students attend college _____

   c) offered training to young people who wanted to work _____

   d) was a kind of domestic peace corps _____

13. What were established to help pay health-care costs for senior citizens and the poor? _____

14. What did Johnson establish in 1966 to help fund public housing projects?

   _____

15. What civil rights law did Johnson persuade Congress to pass? _____

   _____

★ Guided Reading Activity 29-3

DIRECTIONS: Recalling the Facts Use the information in your textbook to answer the questions. Use another sheet of paper if necessary.

1. What new civil rights group was launched by sit-ins? _____

2. Who rode buses in the South to see whether buses were being segregated?

_____

3. Who was the first African American student to enroll at the University of

Mississippi in 1962? _____

4. Why did President John F. Kennedy send federal marshals to escort this student

to the campus? What happened? _____

5. How did Kennedy respond to Governor George Wallace's threat to block the

integration of the University of Alabama in Tuscaloosa? _____

6. When and where did Dr. Martin Luther King, Jr., organize a massive march to

rally support for the civil rights bill? _____

7. What song was becoming an anthem for the civil rights movement?

_____

8. What famous speech did King give at the march? _____

9. What bill ended segregation in stores, restaurants, theaters, and hotels? _____

10. Why did thousands of civil rights workers spread throughout the South during

the summer of 1964? _____

11. What power did the Voting Rights Act of 1965 give the federal government?

_____

12. What Nation of Islam leader at first called for racial separation but later changed

his ideas? _____

13. Who advanced the idea of Black Power? _____

14. What California group symbolized a growing tension between African Americans

and urban police? _____

15. Where did the first, and perhaps the worst, race riot take place in the summer

of 1965? _____

16. When and where was Dr. Martin Luther King, Jr., assassinated? _____

SECTION 29-3

★ **Guided Reading Activity 29-4**

DIRECTIONS: Filling in the Blanks Use your textbook to fill in the blanks using the words in the box. Use another sheet of paper if necessary.

National Organization for Women	**physical disabilities**	**Mexico**
Indian Civil Rights Act of 1968	**United Farm Workers**	**Cuba**
American Indian Movement	**Sandra Day O'Connor**	**New York City**
migrant farmworkers	**feminists**	**César Chávez**
Fidel Castro		

Women's Rights

In 1966 Betty Friedan and other **(1)** _____ created the **(2)** _____, which fought for equal rights for women in all aspects of life. In 1981 President Ronald Reagan appointed **(3)** _____ as the first female justice of the Supreme Court.

Hispanic Americans

The largest Hispanic group in the United States comes from **(4)** _____. The fight for their rights started among Mexican American **(5)** _____. In the early 1960s, the leader of the migrant workers, **(6)** _____, organized thousands of farmworkers into the **(7)** _____. By 1970 Puerto Ricans made up 10 percent of the population of **(8)** _____. More than 200,000 people from **(9)** _____ who opposed the Communist dictator **(10)** _____ fled to the United States in the 1960s.

Native Americans

In the 1960s the National Congress of American Indians sought more control over Native American affairs. Congress passed the **(11)** _____, which formally protected the constitutional rights of all Native Americans. The **(12)** _____ was founded by Clyde Bellecourt, Dennis Banks, and others. In the 1960s and 1970s, Congress passed a number of laws for Americans with **(13)** _____, allowing them more job opportunities, better access to public facilities, and a greater role in society.

★ **Reteaching Activity 29-1**

DIRECTIONS: Organizing Facts The numbered items in the Fact Bank are related to three important events in the civil rights movement. Complete the chart by writing the number of each item in the correct box at the top of the chart. One item fits in two categories. Then answer the questions about Martin Luther King, Jr., in the bottom part of the chart.

The Civil Rights Movement

Brown v. Board of Education of Topeka, Kansas	Little Rock, Arkansas	Montgomery Bus Boycott

Martin Luther King, Jr.

1. During what incident did King emerge as a civil rights leader?

2. How did Mohandas Gandhi's methods influence King?

3. How did the SCLC, which King helped start, prepare African Americans for the struggle for equal rights?

★ **FACT BANK**

1. An African American woman refused to move to the back of a bus.

2. President Dwight D. Eisenhower sent federal troops to protect students.

3. An African American family did not want their child to travel several miles across town to attend school.

4. The Supreme Court ruled that segregation was unconstitutional.

5. December 1952 to May 17, 1954

6. Thurgood Marshall and the NAACP

7. African American students prevented from entering Central High School

8. Rosa Parks

9. December 1, 1955

10. Governor Orval Faubus

11. 1957

12. Linda Brown

★ **Reteaching Activity 29-2**

DIRECTIONS: Completing a Venn Diagram The items in the Fact Bank are associated with John F. Kennedy, Lyndon B. Johnson, or both. Write the letter of each item in the correct section of the diagram.

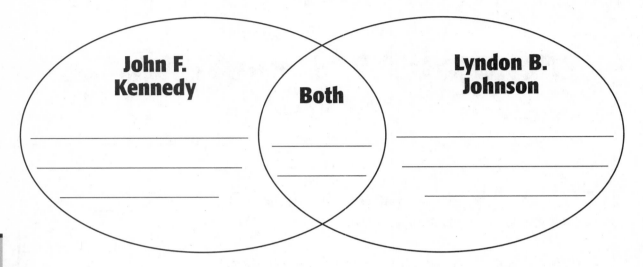

★**FACT BANK**

A. wrote *Profiles in Courage*

B. "... ask not what your country can do for you—ask what you can do for your country"

C. former member of Congress

D. "In a land of great wealth, families must not live in hopeless poverty. In a land rich in harvest, children must not go hungry."

E. assassinated in Dallas, Texas

F. offered the nation youth, energy, and hope

G. "Great Society"

H. Roman Catholic

I. Northerner

J. Declared "an unconditional war on poverty"

K. proposed civil rights legislation

L. established Head Start, Upward Bound, Job Corps, VISTA, and HUD

M. "New Frontier"

N. Southerner

O. commander of a PT boat

DIRECTIONS: Essay On a separate sheet of paper, answer the following questions.

1. How did the televised presidential debates affect the outcome of the 1960 presidential election?

2. What important civil rights bill was passed during the Johnson administration? What did it prohibit? Why did it pass?

★ Reteaching Activity 29-3

DIRECTIONS: Completing a Cluster Each of the numbered items in the Fact Bank provides details about a name in the cluster. Write the correct numbers in the blanks to complete the cluster.

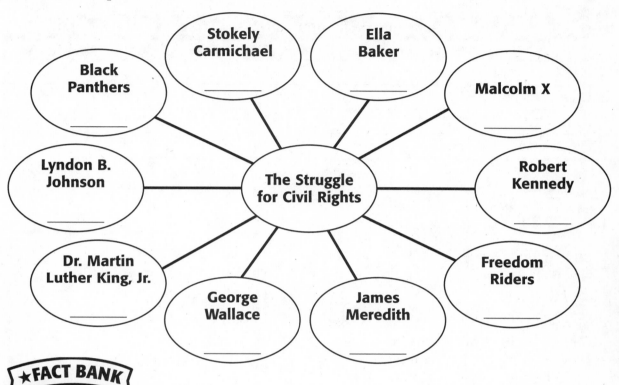

Cluster diagram with central node "The Struggle for Civil Rights" connected to: Black Panthers, Stokely Carmichael, Ella Baker, Malcolm X, Lyndon B. Johnson, Robert Kennedy, Dr. Martin Luther King, Jr., George Wallace, James Meredith, Freedom Riders (each with a blank line)

★FACT BANK

1. governor who vowed to "stand in the schoolhouse door" to block integration of the University of Alabama

2. persuaded Congress to pass the Voting Rights Act of 1965

3. civil rights activist who was the guiding spirit behind the Student Nonviolent Coordinating Committee

4. the first African American to enroll at the University of Mississippi

5. attorney general who advised the president to send the Alabama National Guard to ensure the entry of African American students to the University of Alabama in Tuscaloosa

6. African American leader of SNCC who advanced the idea of Black Power—a philosophy of racial pride

7. civil rights leader who helped organize the march on Washington

8. Nation of Islam leader who was assassinated after changing his ideas of racial separation

9. African American and white CORE members who rode buses in the South to ensure that bus facilities were not being segregated

10. demanded reforms and armed themselves in opposition to urban police

★ Reteaching Activity 29-4

DIRECTIONS: Completing a Chart Write the number of the items from the Fact Bank in the section of the chart where they belong.

Minority Groups Seeking Rights in the United States in the 1960s and 1970s

	Women	Hispanic Americans	Native Americans
People			
Organizations			
Laws			
Events			

★FACT BANK

1. AIM
2. César Chávez
3. Betty Friedan
4. NCAI
5. Nationwide boycotts by consumers who refused to buy some produce led to higher wages and shorter hours for farmworkers.
6. Clyde Bellecourt
7. Roberto Clemente
8. Protests at Alcatraz Island and Wounded Knee, South Dakota, called national attention to their problems.
9. 1975 extension of voting rights

10. NOW
11. United Farm Workers (UFW)
12. Herman Badillo
13. Indian Civil Rights Act of 1968
14. Feminists
15. Equal Pay Act
16. Russell Means
17. Cubans fled to the United States to escape Fidel Castro.
18. People argued that the Equal Rights Amendment would upset the traditional roles of society and lead to the breakdown of the family. The amendment was not ratified.

DIRECTIONS: Essay On a separate sheet of paper, answer the following question.

Describe the laws passed in the 1960s and 1970s in the United States for people with physical disabilities.

★ Enrichment Activity 29-1

Civil Rights Court Decisions

The Supreme Court has passed judgments on many civil rights cases. The time line shows some important cases and the Court's decision.

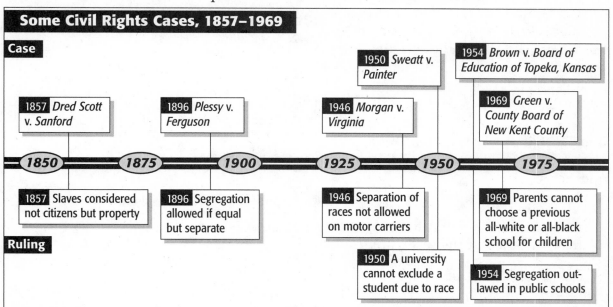

Some Civil Rights Cases, 1857–1969

Case

1950 *Sweatt* v. *Painter*

1954 *Brown* v. *Board of Education of Topeka, Kansas*

1857 *Dred Scott* v. *Sanford*

1896 *Plessy* v. *Ferguson*

1946 *Morgan* v. *Virginia*

1969 *Green* v. *County Board of New Kent County*

1850   **1875**   **1900**   **1925**   **1950**   **1975**

1857 Slaves considered not citizens but property

1896 Segregation allowed if equal but separate

1946 Separation of races not allowed on motor carriers

1969 Parents cannot choose a previous all-white or all-black school for children

1950 A university cannot exclude a student due to race

1954 Segregation outlawed in public schools

Ruling

DIRECTIONS: Interpreting a Time Line Use the time line to answer the following questions.

1. In what year was *Plessy* v. *Ferguson* decided? _____

2. Which case was decided four years after *Morgan* v. *Virginia*? _____

_____

3. Which case established integration in public schools? _____

4. How many years passed between the rulings for desegregation on motor carriers

and desegregation in public schools? _____

5. Which case did *Brown* v. *Board of Education of Topeka, Kansas* overrule? _____

_____

Activity   **DIRECTIONS: Writing an Opinion** You are a Supreme Court justice listening to the case of *Green* v. *County Board of New Kent County.* You have been chosen to write the majority opinion that parents should not be able to choose to send their children to a particular previously all-white or all-African American school. Research Supreme Court opinions to find out how majority opinions are written.

SECTION 29-1

95

★ Enrichment Activity 29-2

Presidential Succession

When a United States president dies in office, the country needs a new president. Rather than hold elections, another official immediately becomes president. The chart on the right shows the entire sequence of presidential succession, the majority of whom are appointed officials.

DIRECTIONS: Interpreting a Chart
Use the chart to answer the following questions.

1. Who would become president if both the president and the vice president died at the same time?

   _____

   _____

2. Who precedes the Secretary of Labor in succession to the presidency?

   _____

   _____

3. Who follows the Secretary of Transportation in succession to the

   presidency?_____

4. Who is fourth in the sequence of succession to the presidency? _____

   _____

The Sequence of Presidential Succession
1. Vice President
2. Speaker of the House
3. President Pro Tempore of the Senate
4. Secretary of State
5. Secretary of the Treasury
6. Secretary of Defense
7. Attorney General
8. Secretary of the Interior
9. Secretary of Agriculture
10. Secretary of Commerce
11. Secretary of Labor
12. Secretary of Health and Human Services
13. Secretary of Housing and Urban Development
14. Secretary of Transportation
15. Secretary of Energy
16. Secretary of Education

SECTION 29-2

Activity

DIRECTIONS: Preparing a Plan Do you agree with the order of succession for the presidency? For example, do you think that presidential succession should be limited to elected officials? Prepare a plan that you think is fair for presidential succession. Compare your plan with those of your classmates and explain why you think it is important for the country to have this sequence of succession to the presidency. Then negotiate and vote on a plan of presidential succession with your classmates.

★ Enrichment Activity 29-3

Struggling for Civil Rights

Many events in the struggle for civil rights occurred between 1954 and 1980. Use your textbook to write the dates for the following events. Include the month and year if possible. Then fill in the time line.

1. _____ Martin Luther King, Jr., leads marches in Birmingham, Alabama.

2. _____ CORE members begin Freedom Rides.

3. _____ The first sit-in takes place in Greensboro, North Carolina.

4. _____ The Civil Rights Act of 1964 is passed.

5. _____ The Voting Rights Act is passed.

6. _____ Martin Luther King, Jr., organizes Washington, D.C., march.

7. _____ Demonstrations on right to vote begin in Selma, Alabama.

8. _____ During Freedom Summer, workers help African Americans register to vote.

Time Line Title:

Years Covered:

Activity **DIRECTIONS: Creating an Illustrated Time Line** Use your completed time line and other outside sources to make a large illustrated time line of the struggle for civil rights. Use the events and their dates listed above and drawings, photographs, or symbols to complete the time line. Add other dates and events if you wish. Display your time lines in the classroom.

SECTION 29-3

★ Enrichment Activity 29-4

Rights for the Menominee

The Menominee have lived for 5,000 years in the same region of Wisconsin. In 1954 the Menominee Termination Act was passed, and the federal government began cutting down trees for housing lots and trying to change the people's cultural identity. With the help of Ada Deer, the act was overturned in 1973, and the Menominee reclaimed their tribal culture and self-determination. Read the excerpt from Ada Deer.

Growing up on the Menominee Reservation in Wisconsin and living in a log cabin on the banks of the Wolf River, like my ancestors before me, I absorbed a deep love and respect for the land and for all living things—trees, plants, and birds, to name but a few. This legacy, so precious to all of us, is central to being Indian. . . .

SOURCE: Viola, Herman J. *After Columbus, The Smithsonian Chronicle of the North American Indians.* Smithsonian Books. Washington, D.C.

DIRECTIONS: Recalling Facts Answer the following questions in the space provided.

1. Where did the Menominee live? _____

2. When was the Menominee Termination Act passed and what did the act seek to do?

_____

3. How long had the Menominee lived in the same location?_____

4. What does Ada Deer say is "central to being Indian"? _____

Activity **DIRECTIONS: Creating a Drawing** Create a drawing or a painting that captures the images and feelings expressed in Ada Deer's description of her childhood lands. Then draw another picture to show what might have happened to the area if the Menominee Termination Act had not been overruled.

SECTION 29-4

Chapter 30 Resources

CHAPTER 30

★ Vocabulary Activity 30

DIRECTIONS: Matching Select the term that matches each definition below. Write the correct term in the space provided.

credibility gap	escalate	executive order	coup
silent majority	counterculture	Vietcong	MIAs
exile	deferment	flexible response	search-and-destroy mission

1. A plan, introduced by President John F. Kennedy, which relied on special military units trained to fight guerrilla wars _____

2. A rule issued by someone such as a president _____

3. A person forced from his or her home country _____

4. Members of the National Liberation Front _____

5. The overthrow of a government _____

6. To gradually increase _____

7. Army maneuver in which troops seek out enemy units and then eliminate them _____

8. Movement that rejected traditional American values _____

9. It excused someone from serving in the military _____

10. Public doubt about the truth of statements from officials _____

11. People who Richard M. Nixon said were the nonshouters and nondemonstrators during the Vietnam War _____

12. American soldiers classified as missing in action _____

DIRECTIONS: Using Vocabulary Use each of the following terms correctly in a complete sentence. Write the sentences on a separate sheet of paper.

hot line	dove	hawk	radical	martial law
blockade	guerrilla warfare	domino theory	Vietnamization	

★ Chapter Skills Activity 30

Building a Database

An electronic database program can help you organize and manage a large amount of information. Once you enter data in a database table, you can quickly locate a record according to key information. If you have a newspaper delivery route, for example, you could have the program list all your customers that live on a particular street. You could also locate all customers who receive newspapers on weekends only.

DIRECTIONS: Building a Database Table Use the information about the Vietnam War in the chapter to create a database of key events in the war from 1965 to 1973. Complete the database table below by filling in the key event or events, the number of United States troops in Vietnam that year, and the name of the United States president at the time. If figures are not given in the text, use the graph on page 886 in your textbook to get an estimate of troop strength.

Year	Event	President	Troop Strength
1965			
1966			
1967			
1968			
1969			
1970			
1971			
1972			
1973			

CRITICAL THINKING

Analyzing Information In the table above, the year is displayed chronologically in the first column. Why might it be helpful to display troop strength?

_____

Critical Thinking Skills Activity 30 | Making Inferences

SOCIAL STUDIES OBJECTIVE: Analyze information by making inferences

LEARNING THE SKILL

An inference is a conclusion that you draw based on known facts or data. For example, you might learn that Communist-nationalist forces in Vietnam fought against both France and the United States between the 1950s and 1970s. If you then learn that Vietnam has a Communist government today, you can *infer* that the fighting never dislodged the Communist forces. Making inferences goes beyond what you see on the page to find answers or to analyze what is occurring during a particular period in history.

APPLYING THE SKILL

DIRECTIONS: Use the table to answer the following questions.

Date	Mission
1957	Soviet Union (USSR) launches the first satellite, *Sputnik*.
1958	U.S. government forms NASA (National Aeronautics and Space Administration) to carry out a program of space exploration.
1959 (Sept.)	USSR launches *Luna 2*, the first probe to hit the moon
1961 (April)	USSR cosmonaut Yuri Gagarin becomes the first person to orbit Earth
1961 (May)	Alan Shepard becomes the first U.S. astronaut in space
1962	John Glenn becomes the first U.S. astronaut to orbit Earth
1963	USSR cosmonaut Valentina Tereshkova becomes the first woman in space
1969	U.S. astronaut Neil Armstrong becomes the first human on the moon
1981	U.S. launches *Columbia*, the first reusable space shuttle rocket
1985	European Space Agency launches *Giotto* probe, which flies by and photographs Halley's Comet in 1986
1986	First module of the Soviet space station *Mir*, site of several joint American-Soviet space missions, is put into orbit.
1997 (July)	*Mars Pathfinder* begins three months of image transmission from Mars surface; carries Sojourner rover that analyzes Martian rocks and soil
1998	Launch of the first module of the International Space Station, a joint project of 15 nations including the United States and Russia

1. Why do you think the United States formed a government agency to oversee space exploration in 1958?

_____

_____

2. In the late 1950s and early 1960s, did the United States or the Soviet Union have more accomplishments in space exploration? Explain your answer.

_____

_____

CHAPTER 30

Critical Thinking Skills Activity 30 | Making Inferences

3. The United States and the Soviet Union sent their first astronauts into orbit around Earth rather than deep into space. Why was this the case?

_____

_____

4. Why have several recent NASA spacecraft, including the 1997 *Mars Pathfinder*, been sent to Mars rather than the moon?

_____

_____

5. Using the data in the table, determine how the organization of space exploration in the late 1950s and early 1960s was different from its organization from the mid-1980s onward.

_____

_____

PRACTICING THE SKILL

DIRECTIONS: In the blank at the left, write the letter of the choice that best answers the question.

_____ **1.** How was Alan Shepard's 1961 mission different from John Glenn's 1962 mission?
  A. Glenn was in orbit much longer than Shepard.
  B. Shepard's mission was a failure.
  C. Shepard went into space, but not into orbit.
  D. There was no difference in the two missions.

_____ **2.** What does the 1986 chart entry on *Mir* tell you about the United States and Soviet space programs at the time?
  A. The competition between the two space programs was at its peak.
  B. The Soviet Union was about to end its space program.
  C. The United States and the Soviet Union were cooperating in some areas of space exploration.
  D. There were no longer moons and planets to explore.

_____ **3.** What can you infer from the launch of the *Giotto* probe?
  A. Halley's Comet was first discovered in 1986.
  B. Neither the Americans nor the Soviets could build a probe to reach the comet.
  C. The European Space Agency was only interested in studying comets.
  D. Countries other than the United States and the Soviet Union had begun to explore space.

★ GEOGRAPHY AND HISTORY ACTIVITY 30

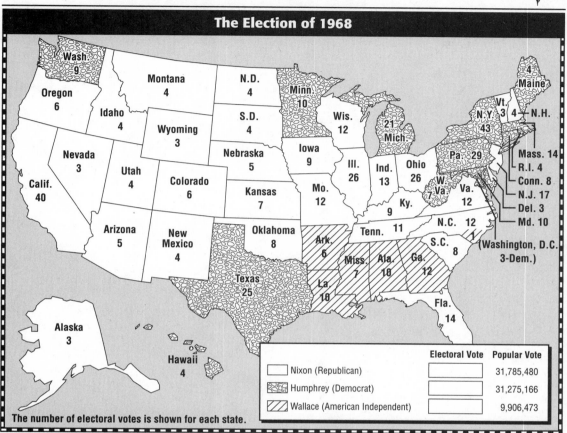

The number of electoral votes is shown for each state.

CHAPTER 30

DIRECTIONS: Write your answers to questions 1–4 on the map. You may abbreviate if you wish.

1. In the 1968 election, the winner needed at least 270 electoral votes. Write the number of electoral votes each candidate received in the correct spot in the map key.

2. Determine in which part of the country Hubert Humphrey received the most electoral votes. Use red to color the states won by Humphrey in this region.

3. Outline in black the three states that gave Humphrey more than half his electoral votes.

4. If Humphrey had won all the electoral votes that went to George C. Wallace, in addition to his own, the electoral votes of one additional state would have given him the necessary 270 majority of electoral votes to win the election. Color that state blue.

5. What can you conclude about the populations of Texas and New Mexico from the

   contrasting information on this map? _____

   _____

★ **Time Line Activity 30**

United States Conflict with Cuba (1959–1962)

DIRECTIONS: Read the following background information. Then examine the time line. Use what you learn to answer the questions in the spaces provided.

UNITED STATES-CUBAN RELATIONS

Jan. 1959 Fulgencio Batista is overthrown by Fidel Castro's guerrillas in Cuba

March 1960 Dwight D. Eisenhower approves a CIA plan for an invasion of Cuba

Jan. 1961 Newly elected President John F. Kennedy allows CIA plan to proceed

April 1961 United States-trained Cuban exiles land at the Bay of Pigs; invasion fails

Dec. 1961 Castro declares he is a Marxist-Leninist and aligns Cuba with the Soviet Union

Oct. 1961 Kennedy imposes a naval blockade of Cuba during the Cuban missile crisis

Dec. 1962 Castro releases Bay of Pigs prisoners for $53 million worth of drugs and food from the United States

1958 1959 1960 1961 1962

UNITED STATES FOREIGN POLICY IN CUBA

☑ Background

The Central Intelligence Agency (CIA) plan to overthrow the revolutionary regime of Fidel Castro in Cuba put into motion a series of critical events. The utter failure of the invasion of the Bay of Pigs in Cuba jeopardized United States relations with Latin America and the Soviet Union. The Cold War confrontation between the United States and the Soviet Union was underscored by the Cuban missile crisis.

1. What Cuban dictator was overthrown by Fidel Castro in 1959?

_____

2. During which United States president's administration did the CIA devise a plan to overthrow Fidel Castro?

_____

3. When did the Bay of Pigs invasion take place?

_____

4. When did President John F. Kennedy impose a naval blockade on Cuba?

_____

5. When did Castro's Cuba align itself with the Soviet Union?

_____

6. Under what conditions did Castro agree to release political prisoners in 1962?

_____

CHAPTER 30

Linking Past and Present Activity 30

Vietnam War

 **THEN** In the early 1960s, the United States became involved in a battle against communism in Southeast Asia. The Vietnam War was a military conflict between the United States-backed South Vietnamese government and the Communist-led guerrilla forces backed by North Vietnam. The war was America's longest ever. By the time it ended in 1975, more than 58,000 Americans had died, about 300,000 were wounded, and millions of Vietnamese civilians were killed, wounded, or left homeless.

Public opinion about the United States's participation in the war was sharply and bitterly divided. Many people who fought in the conflict also questioned the reasons for the nation's involvement.

When American troops returned home from Vietnam, they were not welcomed with the joyous celebrations that had greeted earlier war veterans. Instead Vietnam veterans returned to an indifference that sometimes bordered on hostility. The long and controversial Vietnam War left behind anger and division in segments of American society.

NOW Today the Vietnam Veterans War Memorial in Washington, D.C., publicly recognizes and honors the American men and women who served in the Vietnam War. "The Wall," designed by Maya Lin, opened on Veterans Day, November 13, 1982. Chiseled on the 500-foot, shiny, black marble, V-shaped wall are the names of every American killed or missing in the war. The names are arranged chronologically by the date of death and begin and end in the center of the memorial. Thus, the war's beginning and end meet, symbolizing how the Vietnam War has come full circle.

The Vietnam Veterans War Memorial is one of the most-visited sites in the nation's capital. Visitors touch the names and leave medals, letters, photos, and other mementos by the wall each day.

Activity

DIRECTIONS: Designing a Memorial Who are your heroes? Make a list of at least five people who are no longer living, whom you consider heroes. You might include relatives, people you have read about in *The American Journey*, celebrities, or community leaders. Design a memorial to honor one of the individuals on your list. Draw the memorial, create a clay model, or make a diorama.

★ Primary Source Reading 30

Letter from Vietnam

> ✪ **Interpreting the Source** This letter was dictated to a Red Cross volunteer by Second Lieutenant Fred Downs, who lost his left arm to a land mine in January 1968. As you read, think about the writer's attitude.

Dear Linda,

Some good news today. Doctor said that I wouldn't have to lose my right arm and will be able to regain almost full control. . . .

. . . The day or so after I got hit, one of my men stepped on the same kind of mine I did and was killed. In the space of five days I lost 16 men in my platoon to mines. One KIA [Killed in Action] and the rest WIA [Wounded in Action]—quite a few will lose their legs and maybe a couple their hands. My good friend . . . Bill Ordway, was killed two days after my accident. . . .

After seeing the patients around me, I consider myself very lucky. There are many who have lost legs, arms, eyes and other parts of their bodies, which leaves them in worse shape than I am. I'm really very anxious to know how you feel about me losing my arm because naturally I don't know how you will react when you see me. With my new arm they will give me, I'll be able to act like I normally did, which was always a little crazy. I haven't been depressed or anything like that, so [I] don't want you to feel bad either. I just paid the price that many soldiers pay defending our country, and I've accepted the fact that I can get along as well with an artificial arm as I did before. Some guys feel so sorry for themselves. They're miserable all the time. But our mind and soul don't come from our extremities. My personality is the same as it's always been and is not going to change because of a little setback.

Tell Tammy and Teri that I miss them and look forward to seeing [them] both very much. . . . I love you and miss you very much.

Your husband,
Fred

SOURCE: *Dear America: Letters Home from Vietnam,* edited by Bernard Edelman for the New York Vietnam Veterans Memorial Commission. NY: W.W. Norton, 1985.

DOCUMENT-BASED QUESTION

DIRECTIONS: Answer the following question on a separate sheet of paper.
How does Fred Downs feel about the loss of his arm?

DIRECTIONS: Writing an Introduction Write the introduction, or foreword, to a book of letters from soldiers in Vietnam. In your foreword, explain why the letters are important to read.

CHAPTER 30

111

Chapter 30 Section Resources

SECTIONS

★ Guided Reading Activity 30-1

DIRECTIONS: Outlining Locate the heading in your textbook. Then use the information under the heading to help you write each answer. Use another sheet of paper if necessary

I. New Directions

   A. Strength Through Flexibility

      1. What tactics did some Communist groups employ to take control of their

      nation's governments? _____

      2. Who were the Green Berets? _____

   B. Strength Through Aid

      1. Why did Kennedy provide aid to some countries in Latin America, Asia,

      and Africa?_____

      2. What did Kennedy create by executive order on March 1, 1961? _____

      3. Why did Kennedy propose the Alliance for Progress? _____

II. Cold War Confrontations

   A. Introduction

      1. When did CIA-trained Cuban exiles invade the Bay of Pigs? _____

      2. What happened when Kennedy refused to provide American air support?

      _____

   B. The Berlin Wall

      1. Why did the East German government erect the Berlin Wall? _____

      2. What did the Berlin Wall symbolize? _____

III. The Cuban Missile Crisis

   A. Introduction

      1. What did American spy planes flying over Cuba in October 1962 discover?

      _____

      2. Why did Kennedy and Nikita Khrushchev create the hot line? _____

   B. Rivalry in Space

      1. Who was the first person to orbit the earth? _____

      2. Who was the first American to make a space flight? Who was the first

      American to orbit the earth? _____

      3. When did Neil Armstrong walk on the moon? _____

SECTION 30-1

★ Guided Reading Activity 30-2

DIRECTIONS: Filling in the Blanks Use your textbook to fill in the blanks using the words in the box. Use another sheet of paper if necessary.

Robert McNamara	**Ho Chi Minh**	**coup**	**French**
Operation Rolling Thunder	**Ho Chi Minh Trail**	**500,000**	**dense jungles**
Gulf of Tonkin Resolution	**November 1, 1963**	**Ngo Dinh Diem**	**Vietcong**
National Liberation Front	**search-and-destroy**	**Geneva Accords**	

The U. S. and Vietnam

After World War II, the Communist leader of Vietnam, **(1)** _____, declared Vietnam's independence. The **(2)** _____ were unwilling to give up their rich Indochina colony; after a long, bloody war, they were defeated by the Communists in 1954. The **(3)** _____ divided Vietnam into Communist North Vietnam and non-Communist South Vietnam. In 1955 **(4)** _____ gained control of the government of South Vietnam. Communist supporters in the South organized themselves as the **(5)** _____, better known to Americans as the **(6)** _____. On **(7)** _____, South Vietnamese army officers staged a **(8)** _____ and assassinated Ngo Dinh Diem.

The Conflict Deepens

In 1964 Congress passed the **(9)** _____, which gave Johnson broad authority to use American forces in Vietnam. About 180,000 soldiers were in Vietnam by the end of 1965, and more than **(10)** _____ by late 1967. The United States unleashed an intense bombing campaign called **(11)** _____ to stop the flow of North Vietnamese troops and equipment into South Vietnam. American troops found fighting difficult because of **(12)** _____, muddy trails, and swampy rice paddies. The bombing of the **(13)** _____ and the North did not stop the constant flow of troops and equipment south. The **(14)** _____ missions killed thousands of enemy troops, but the troops always seemed to be replaced. As American soldiers became frustrated and the war dragged on, Secretary of Defense **(15)** _____ began to argue that the war could not be won.

★ Guided Reading Activity 30-3

DIRECTIONS: Recalling the Facts Use the information in your textbook to answer the questions. Use another sheet of paper if necessary.

1. What were the opponents of the Vietnam War called? _____

2. What were the supporters of the Vietnam War called? _____

3. What event in October 1967 showed that opposition to the war was growing?

_____

4. What two major cities in South Vietnam were attacked during the Tet offensive?

_____

5. What negative impact did the Tet offensive have on the Johnson administration?

_____

6. Who were the two antiwar candidates for the Democratic Party's presidential

nomination in 1968? _____

7. What startling announcement did President Lyndon B. Johnson make on

March 31, 1968? _____

8. How did the assassination of Martin Luther King, Jr., affect the country?

_____

9. What Democratic candidate avoided the primaries, seeking support among party

leaders instead? _____

10. Who won the Democratic primary election in California in June 1968? What

happened that same night that sent the nation into shock? _____

11. Where did the Democrats hold their convention in 1968? _____

12. Why did antiwar Democrats protest the convention? _____

13. Who ordered the police out in force at the convention? Why? _____

14. How did the violence at the convention affect the Democratic Party? _____

15. Who ran as a third-party candidate, using a "law-and-order" theme? _____

_____

16. Whom did Republican presidential nominee, Richard M. Nixon, pledge

to represent? _____

17. Why did Nixon win the election? _____

SECTION 30-3

★ **Guided Reading Activity 30-4**

DIRECTIONS: Filling in the Blanks Use your textbook to fill in the blanks using the words in the box. Some words may be used more than once. Use another sheet of paper if necessary.

Vietnam Veterans Memorial	South Vietnam	birth date	Saigon
Kent State University	antiwar protest	Jackson State	58,000
antiwar movement	Henry Kissinger	April 30, 1975	Cambodia
draft deferments	January 27, 1973	Vietnamization	

A New Strategy

Under President Nixon college students could no longer obtain **(1)** _____; only 19 year olds could be called for service in Vietnam; and draftees would be chosen by lottery on the basis of their **(2)** _____. By the end of 1969, Nixon had developed his plan of **(3)** _____, which called for the army of **(4)** _____ to be more active in the fighting. The bombing of enemy supply routes and hideouts in **(5)** _____ and Laos was kept secret from the American people.

Renewed Opposition at Home

In October 1969 more than 300,000 people took part in an **(6)** _____ in Washington, D.C. **(7)** _____ represented the United States in the Paris peace talks. The North Vietnamese believed that the **(8)** _____ in the United States would force the Americans to withdraw. Nixon's decision to attack **(9)** _____ in April 1970 outraged Congress. In May at a campus protest at **(10)** _____ in Kent, Ohio, the National Guard fired on student protesters, killing four. Violence flared again on May 14 at **(11)** _____ in Mississippi, where two students were shot and killed.

"Peace Is at Hand"

In the fall of 1972, North Vietnam and the United States reached a tentative peace agreement. Negotiators signed a peace agreement on **(12)** _____. In early 1975 North Vietnamese forces closed in on **(13)** _____. The city finally fell to the Communists in the early hours of **(14)** _____.

Legacy of the War

More than **(15)** _____ Americans died in the Vietnam War. The construction of the **(16)** _____ in Washington, D.C., helped heal the country's wounds.

★ **Reteaching Activity 30-1**

DIRECTIONS: Identifying Problems and Solutions The pursuit of anti-Communist foreign policy caused problems for both the United States and the Soviet Union during the Kennedy administration. The solutions to some of these problems did not always work and occasionally caused other problems. After each *Problem,* write the letters of the *Solutions* from the Fact Bank.

1. **Problem:** In certain areas of the world, Communist groups used guerrilla tactics to take control of their nation's government.

   Solutions: _____

2. **Problem:** The free governments of poverty-stricken countries in Latin America, Asia, and Africa were vulnerable to Communist overthrow.

   Solutions: _____

3. **Problem:** Fidel Castro formed an alliance with the Soviet Union.

   Solutions: _____

4. **Problem:** The Soviet Union wanted to assert its position in East Germany and stop the flow of East Germans to the West.

   Solutions: _____

5. **Problem:** The Soviets built launching sites for nuclear missiles in Cuba.

   Solutions: _____

6. **Problem:** The buildup and testing of nuclear weapons by the superpowers created a potential for a nuclear disaster.

   Solutions: _____

★**FACT BANK**

A. The CIA recruited a military force from Cuban exiles who had settled in the United States.

B. John F. Kennedy proposed the Alliance for Progress.

C. Kennedy warned the Soviets that an attack against any nation in the Western Hemisphere would be seen as an attack on the United States.

D. Kennedy created the Peace Corps.

E. The Berlin Wall was erected.

F. Kennedy and Nikita Khrushchev created a hot line between Moscow and Washington.

G. The United States and the Soviet Union signed a treaty, banning nuclear tests above ground and underwater.

H. Kennedy introduced a plan called flexible response.

I. Khrushchev told Kennedy that the West must move out of Berlin.

J. American-trained forces invaded Cuba to try to spark an uprising.

K. Kennedy ordered the navy to blockade Cuba.

L. Special military units such as the Green Berets were created.

SECTION 30-1

★ Reteaching Activity 30-2

DIRECTIONS: Sequencing Number the events in the order in which they occurred. Use the same number for events that happened at the same time.

_____ **A.** Robert McNamara travels to Vietnam on a fact-finding mission.

_____ **B.** Vietnamese forces defeat the French in a long, bloody war.

_____ **C.** Ngo Dinh Diem refuses to hold elections in South Vietnam.

_____ **D.** South Vietnamese army officers stage a coup and assassinate Diem.

_____ **E.** The terms of the Geneva Accords divide Vietnam temporarily into North Vietnam and South Vietnam.

_____ **F.** American ground forces conduct search-and-destroy missions to seek out Vietcong; in the air, planes deliver napalm to destroy the jungle growth where the Vietcong hide.

_____ **G.** Ngo Dinh Diem gains control of South Vietnam.

_____ **H.** John F. Kennedy sends Special Forces troops to South Vietnam.

_____ **I.** Congress passes the Gulf of Tonkin Resolution.

_____ **J.** Japanese forces capture the French colony of Indochina.

_____ **K.** Ngo Dinh Diem launches a campaign to destroy the power of the Communist supporters in South Vietnam.

_____ **L.** Robert McNamara begins to argue that the war cannot be won.

_____ **M.** The Vietcong begin a war against the Diem regime.

_____ **N.** The United States becomes the dominant foreign power in South Vietnam.

_____ **O.** United States Marines land near Da Nang as Lyndon B. Johnson begins to escalate United States involvement in Vietnam.

_____ **P.** Ho Chi Minh declares Vietnam's independence.

_____ **Q.** Buddhist monks set themselves on fire on busy South Vietnam streets to show their opposition to the government.

DIRECTIONS: Essay On a separate sheet of paper, answer the following question. Why was the ground war in Vietnam difficult for American troops?

★ **Reteaching Activity 30-3**

DIRECTIONS: Crossword Puzzle Complete the crossword puzzle about how the Vietnam War affected life at home.

Robert F. Kennedy	doves	radical	draft	Vietnam
counterculture	deferments	draft cards	convention	hawks

Across

5. given to excuse college students from serving in the military

8. revolutionary or new

9. opponents of the Vietnam War

Down

1. this antiwar presidential candidate was once the attorney general

2. antiwar Democrats felt angry and excluded from this event in Chicago

3. movement that rejected traditional American values

4. the selective service system

5. military registration forms burned by protesters in the 1960s

6. country where American troops were fighting

7. supporters of the Vietnam War

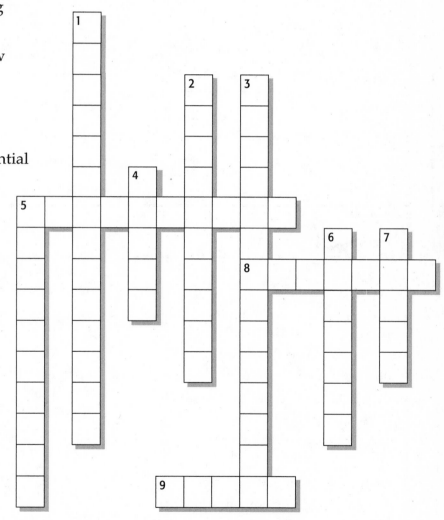

SECTION 30-3

★ **Reteaching Activity 30-4**

DIRECTIONS: Organizing Facts Complete the top part of the chart by writing the number of each item from the Fact Bank related to Richard M. Nixon's peace with honor strategy. Then complete the time lines related to the invasion of Cambodia and the end of the Vietnam War by writing the number of the item that matches each date given.

Nixon's Peace with Honor Strategy

Draft Reform	Vietnamization	Bombing Campaign

The Invasion of Cambodia	The War Ends
April 1970	Fall 1972
May 4, 1970	December 1972
May 14, 1970	January 27, 1973
	Early 1975
	April 30, 1975

★**FACT BANK**

1. The bombing of Cambodia would be a secret.

2. Nixon unleashes the heaviest bombardment of the war on North Vietnam.

3. Protests against the draft fade.

4. College students could no longer obtain draft deferments.

5. Enemy supply routes in Cambodia and Laos would be attacked.

6. Saigon falls to the Communists.

7. Police kill two students at a protest at Jackson State.

8. Nixon decides to send American troops to attack Cambodia.

9. Negotiators at the Paris peace talks sign an agreement.

10. Only 19 year olds could be called for service in Vietnam.

11. The army of South Vietnam would take a more active role in fighting the war.

12. A protest at Kent State turns violent; four students are killed by National Guard members.

13. The last Americans scramble to escape Vietnam.

14. Draftees would be chosen by lottery on the basis of birth date.

15. American ground troops would gradually withdraw, lowering their number to 60,000 by 1971.

16. Henry Kissinger announces "Peace is at hand."

SECTION 30-4

★ Enrichment Activity 30-1

The Peace Corps

Between 1961 and 1989, Peace Corps volunteers served in many countries of the world. Most of the countries were located in South America, Central America, Africa, and Asia. The map on the right shows countries in the region called *Inter-America* by the Peace Corps.

Countries with Peace Corps Workers, 1961–1989

GUATEMALA
BELIZE
HONDURAS
NICARAGUA
EL SALVADOR
COSTA RICA
PANAMA
ECUADOR
COLOMBIA
TURKS AND CAICOS ISLANDS
HAITI
DOMINICAN REPUBLIC
VENEZUELA
EASTERN CARIBBEAN
GRENADA
GUYANA
BRAZIL
PERU
BOLIVIA
CHILE
PARAGUAY
URUGUAY
ATLANTIC OCEAN
PACIFIC OCEAN

N
W ◇ E
S

Countries with Peace Corps workers

DIRECTIONS: Interpreting a Map Use the map to answer the following questions.

1. Name four Central American countries that had Peace Corps workers.

_____

_____

_____

2. How many countries in South America had Peace Corps workers? _____

3. About what percentage of all the countries of South America had Peace Corps help?

_____

4. Which South American countries did not have Peace Corps help? (You may need

to use another map to find the names.) _____

Activity

DIRECTIONS: Making a Scrapbook You are a Peace Corps volunteer in the 1960s. Choose the country in the Inter-American region. In order for you to become familiar with the tasks, language, and culture, begin assembling materials about that country. Try to identify the needs of the country and to include information about the culture. Present the information that you have collected to the class.

SECTION 30-1

121

★ Enrichment Activity 30-2

The War in Vietnam

The outline map to the rights shows Vietnam. Study the map. Use your textbook or an atlas to complete the activity that follows.

Activity **DIRECTIONS:** Follow the directions to complete the map. You may abbreviate if you wish.

1. Label North Vietnam and South Vietnam.

2. The Gulf of Tonkin lies to the east of North Vietnam, and the South China Sea lies to the east of South Vietnam. Label these two bodies of water.

3. The Ho Chi Minh Trail ran approximately north-south from Vinh in North Vietnam through Laos and Cambodia to Tay Ninh in South Vietnam. Label the Ho Chi Minh Trail, Laos, and Cambodia.

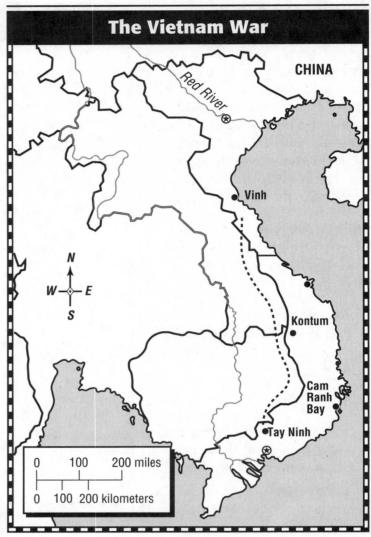

The Vietnam War

CHINA

Red River

Vinh

Kontum

Cam Ranh Bay

Tay Ninh

N
W E
S

0   100   200 miles

0   100 200 kilometers

4. Label Da Nang, which lies on the northeast coast of South Vietnam.

5. Label Saigon, which lies along the east coast of southern South Vietnam in a large bay.

6. Label Hanoi, which lies inland on the Red River in North Vietnam.

7. The Mekong River forms the border between Laos and Thailand and flows through Cambodia into the Mekong Delta at the southern tip of South Vietnam. Label the Mekong River, Thailand, and the Mekong Delta.

★ Enrichment Activity 30-3

A Different War

The year 1968 was important in NASA's Apollo program, which was racing to send United States astronauts to the moon. *Apollo-Saturn 7* accomplished the first piloted flight of the command-service module. The event was shown on public television in October 1968. *Apollo-Saturn 8*, in December 1968, made the first lunar orbit by United States astronauts. Television viewers got their first live close-up glimpse of the moon on television. Study the diagram of the *Apollo* rocket on the right.

DIRECTIONS: Recalling Facts Use the information provided and the diagram to answer the following questions.

1. What event was shown on public television in October of 1968?

_____

2. Which United States spacecraft made the first lunar orbit?

_____

3. How many stages did that rocket have?

_____

4. What fuel combinations did each stage

use? _____

Activity **DIRECTIONS: Making a Collage** On a separate sheet of paper, redraw the rocket from the diagram provided. Then make a poster entitled "Space Exploration" by developing a collage of space exploration images around your drawing. Use the media center to find newspaper accounts from the period. Include important dates, images, and interesting bits of information in your collage.

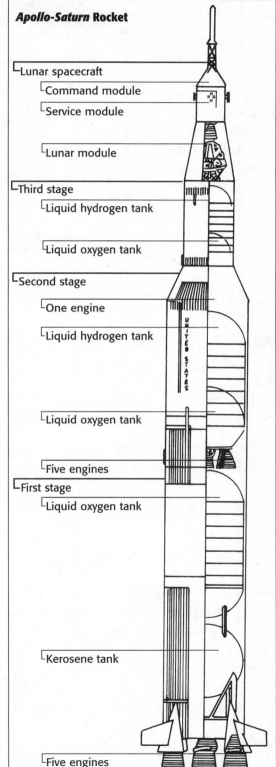

Apollo-Saturn Rocket

- Lunar spacecraft
  - Command module
  - Service module
  - Lunar module
- Third stage
  - Liquid hydrogen tank
  - Liquid oxygen tank
- Second stage
  - One engine
  - Liquid hydrogen tank
  - Liquid oxygen tank
  - Five engines
- First stage
  - Liquid oxygen tank
  - Kerosene tank
  - Five engines

★ Enrichment Activity 30-4

Prisoners and MIAs

Many military personnel were taken prisoners or were missing in action during the Vietnam War. The graph shows prisoners and MIAs for four branches of the military between 1965 and 1973.

United States Military Personnel Taken as Prisoners or Missing in Action, 1965–1973

SOURCE: *The Encyclopedia of Military History from 3500 B.C. to the Present.* Harper and Row, New York.

DIRECTIONS: Interpreting a Graph Use the graph to answer the following questions.

1. Which branch of the military had the greatest number of personnel taken as prisoners and missing in action during the years shown? _____

2. What was the total of personnel taken as prisoners and missing in action from all four branches of the military? _____

3. How many more Air Force personnel were taken as prisoners and missing in action than Marines? _____

4. What percentage of the total of personnel taken as prisoners and missing in action was made up of army personnel? _____

Activity

DIRECTIONS: Making a Graph The order from most to least of total personnel serving in Vietnam during those years was as follows: Army, Marines, Air Force, Navy. Research to find the total personnel who served in Vietnam in each of the branches. What percentage of each branch was missing in action or taken prisoner in Vietnam? Present the information in a circle graph. Write a brief explanation of your graph.

CITIZENSHIP ACTIVITY 10

Questions to Ask

1. The civil rights of individuals are protected both by amendments to the Constitution and by other federal laws.

2. the Fifteenth, Nineteenth, and Twenty-fourth Amendments

3. Student responses may vary, but may include the Fifteenth Amendment, giving fathers of all races the right to vote; the Nineteenth Amendment, giving mothers the right to vote; the Civil Rights Act of 1964, ordering all restaurants and businesses to serve people of all races and religions; or the Equal Opportunity Employment Act, making employment discrimination illegal.

4. Answers may vary, but should include the installation of wheelchair ramps to doorways and the construction of large bathroom stalls with support rails.

ECONOMICS AND HISTORY ACTIVITY 10

Buying Power

1. Farm income generally declined or remained the same.

2. Chuck roast cost 50 cents per pound in 1955. The price increased to 62 cents per pound in 1960, or an increase of 12 cents.

3. Butter had a slight increase in price from 1951 to 1953. Then it returned to its 1950 price and remained about that price until 1965.

4. Farm families could probably not buy what families in the suburbs and cities were buying because the income of the farm families did not significantly increase from 1950 to 1965.

Critical Thinking

Students should show an understanding that with a higher income in the cities and suburbs and a lack of increase in income from farming, more people would have left farming and moved into urban areas to make more money.

AMERICAN LITERATURE READING 10

1. It has been 30 years since Brave Orchid and Moon Orchid have seen each other.

2. Brave Orchid thinks her son is in Vietnam because she suspects that he and her other children have been concealing his whereabouts; whenever his letters come in, they hide the envelopes. Also, Brave Orchid senses that he is on a ship in Da Nang when she mentally sends him help.

3. Answers will vary. Most students will say that she loves her son deeply, and that her criticism of his actions stems from her fear of losing him.

4. Answers will vary. Some students will say that Brave Orchid feels sorry for them because she feels that they do not realize the danger that they are about to face. Her impressions of their innocence are revealed by the fact that some of the soldiers remind her of little Boy Scouts and baby chicks.

5. Answers will vary but might include concern about personal survival and separation from loved ones.

INTERDISCIPLINARY ACTIVITY 10

1. An infectious disease is a disease that spreads easily from one person to another.

2. If the virus enters the central nervous system, it attacks the nerves that control motor activity and can cause paralysis.

3. Jonas Salk developed a vaccine for the disease in the early 1950s. A nation-wide effort followed to vaccinate all Americans.

4. Sabin developed an oral polio vaccine.

5. Answers may include: AIDS, cancer, heart disease, diabetes.

6. Answers will vary, but students might mention that as the diseases have become less common, and side effects from the diseases themselves have become easier to treat, people may be less diligent in seeing that children are vaccinated.

Activity: Answers will vary but may include measles, mumps, chicken pox, polio, diphtheria, whooping cough, and smallpox, among others.

HANDS-ON HISTORY ACTIVITY 10

1. Answers will vary but will probably be from one-half to three-quarters cup.

2. Answers will vary. Students might note that the peanut butter made using a blender is smoother, while the hand-rolled variety is more like crunchy style peanut butter. Making peanut butter with a blender is easier and faster. Students might observe that almost anything done the old-fashioned way takes longer. Taste will be a matter of personal preference.

3. Adding honey to the peanut butter not only makes it sweeter, but also has a slight emulsifying action. Peanut butter with honey may be less likely to separate.

4. Answers will vary. Commercial peanut butter may be more uniform and sweeter. Students' peanut butter may taste more like fresh peanuts.

5. It made it more accessible.

VOCABULARY ACTIVITY 27

1. containment

2. airlift

3. inflation

4. stalemate

5. demilitarized zone

6. subversion

7. blacklist

8. perjury

9. allege

10. censure

11. Winston Churchill first used the phrase "iron curtain" in a speech he made in Fulton, Missouri, in 1946. He said that an "iron curtain" had descended on Europe. He meant that the Soviets had cut off Eastern Europe from the West. Behind this iron curtain lay the countries of Eastern Europe that were part of the Soviet sphere and controlled by Moscow.

12. The Cold War between the United States and the Soviet Union referred to the buildup of each nation's military forces and arms in an attempt to intimidate the other.

13. A closed shop was a workplace that hired only union members.

CHAPTER SKILLS ACTIVITY 27

1. The author probably wanted to emphasize that the United States did not divide after the Civil War and that it is one strong nation.

2. In 1892 there was not equality for all. Women and African Americans did not have the same rights as white men.

3. that this is not just one type of political order, but the actual government that makes the United States what it is— free and democratic

ANSWER KEY

4. Answers may include: Eisenhower believed in God; he wanted the pledge to serve as a prayer; he believed that God protected us; he believed that the United States answered to a higher power.

Activity
Students should show a clear understanding of the difference between information that is presented and information that is implied.

CRITICAL THINKING SKILLS ACTIVITY 27

Applying the Skill

1. It tried to deal with the threat of communism in the United States.

2. According to the acts, the government considered Communists disloyal agents of a foreign power who wished to overthrow the government of the United States.

3. It was not entitled to any of the rights and privileges of other legal bodies in the United States, which students can infer to mean it was not to have had the rights and privileges of other political parties.

4. Accept all reasonable answers. Students should conclude that the laws by themselves, with no other background information about communism in the United

States in the 1950s, would not be enough to form an accurate account. They may infer, however, that the sources provide evidence that people felt threatened by communism and actively tried to prevent it from spreading.

Practicing the Skill
1. C
2. D
3. A

GEOGRAPHY AND HISTORY ACTIVITY 27

1. Turkey should be labeled "farthest east."

2. The number 12 should be written on the NATO countries of Western Europe; 8 should be written on the Warsaw Pact countries of Eastern Europe.

3. East Germany, Czechoslovakia, Albania, and Bulgaria should be colored red.

4. Spain, Ireland, Sweden, Switzerland, Austria, and Yugoslavia should be colored blue.

5. The free nations of Europe and the Communist countries each feared the other group would attack them. Each alliance was formed for mutual support and defense.

TIME LINE ACTIVITY 27

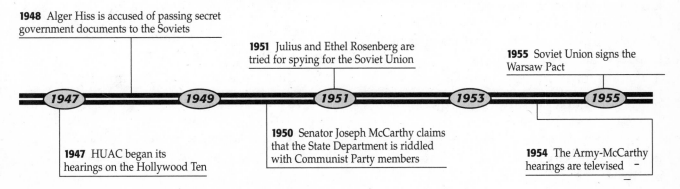

THE RED SCARE IN THE UNITED STATES

1948 Alger Hiss is accused of passing secret government documents to the Soviets

1951 Julius and Ethel Rosenberg are tried for spying for the Soviet Union

1955 Soviet Union signs the Warsaw Pact

1947 — 1949 — 1951 — 1953 — 1955

1947 HUAC began its hearings on the Hollywood Ten

1950 Senator Joseph McCarthy claims that the State Department is riddled with Communist Party members

1954 The Army-McCarthy hearings are televised

LINKING PAST AND PRESENT ACTIVITY 27

Contributors to Modern Personal Computing

Person	Contribution
Jack S. Kilby	Developed modular and integrated circuit technology at Texas Instruments
Grace Murray Hopper	Pioneered the use of computer language programming compilers to make computers more user-friendly. Her work led to the UNIVAC computer and COBOL programming language
William (Bill) Gates III	With Paul Allen developed BASIC programming language interpreter for personal computers and cofounded Microsoft Corporation, one of the world's largest software developers
Steven P. Jobs	Codesigned Apple II computer and cofounded Apple Computer, Inc., with Steve Wozniak
Paul Barans	Conceived of a "fishnet" type of computer communications network. His idea eventually led to development of the Internet

PRIMARY SOURCE READING ACTIVITY 27

Document-Based Question

He is trying to imply that Soviet Russia is strongly influencing the politics and people from the Baltic to the Adriatic, a large area that contains many great cities.

Students' maps need not be drawn to scale but should show the general shape of the European continent. They may use additional sources to draw the line "from Stettin in the Baltic to Trieste in the Adriatic." Cities shown should include Warsaw, Berlin, Prague, Vienna, Budapest, Belgrade, Bucharest, and Sofia.

GUIDED READING ACTIVITY 27-1

1. Franklin D. Roosevelt, Winston Churchill, Joseph Stalin
2. Yalta (a Soviet port on the Black Sea)
3. Soviets agreed to join the war against Japan; in return, the Soviets received territory in Asia.
4. into four zones; the Soviet Union, the United States, Great Britain, and France each controlled one zone
5. June 26, 1945, San Francisco, California
6. the Soviet-controlled Communist governments of the East and the capitalist democracies of the Western nations
7. Winston Churchill; He meant that the Soviets had cut off Eastern Europe from the West.
8. containment
9. a commitment to help nations threatened by communism and Soviet expansion
10. George Marshall; the Marshall Plan
11. The West had announced plans to unite their zones to form a new West German republic on June 7.
12. He organized the Berlin airlift.
13. the Federal Republic of Germany (West Germany) and the German Democratic Republic (East Germany)
14. that the United States and the Soviet Union were locked in a cold war
15. the formation of NATO and the Warsaw Pact
16. to divide Palestine into independent Jewish and Arab states with Jerusalem as an international city

17. Mao Zedong, who led the Communist forces, was victorious and formed the People's Republic of China; Chiang Kai-shek, who led the Chinese government forces, retreated to Taiwan.

GUIDED READING ACTIVITY 27-2

I. A. the removal of price controls and a huge increase in consumer demand and spending

B. Labor unions called strikes.

C. He had the government take over the mines; he persuaded mine owners to grant workers' demands.

II. A. 1. "Had Enough?"

2. Taft-Hartley bill

B. aggressively, traveling more than 30,000 miles on a whistle-stop tour of the country, giving speeches attacking Congress

C. laws to raise the minimum wage, expand Social Security benefits for senior citizens, and provide funds for housing for low-income families

III. A. He ordered federal departments and agencies to end job discrimination against African Americans and ordered the armed forces to desegregate; he also instructed the Justice Department to actively enforce existing civil rights laws.

B. the clearance of slums, government-backed medical insurance, higher minimum wages, and more federal money for public schools

GUIDED READING ACTIVITY 27-3

1. 38th parallel

2. June 25, 1950

3. "police action"

4. containment

5. United Nations

6. General Douglas MacArthur

7. Inchon

8. Seoul

9. Pyongyang

10. Chinese

11. Chinese troops

12. Seoul

13. stalemate

14. General Douglas MacArthur

15. July 27, 1953

16. demilitarized zone

GUIDED READING ACTIVITY 27-4

1. Americans' fears of Communist subversion

2. "Reds"

3. Red Scare

4. all Communist organizations to register with the government and to provide lists of members

5. House Un-American Activities Committee (HUAC)

6. anti-Communist hysteria

7. screenwriters and directors who went to jail for refusing to answer questions about their political beliefs or those of their colleagues

8. lists, created by film companies, of individuals whose loyalty to the nation was suspicious; they were used to bar people from working in Hollywood

9. Alger Hiss, a former State Department official

10. a New York couple, who were members of the Communist Party, accused of plotting to pass secret information about the atomic bomb to the Soviet Union

11. They were convicted and sentenced to death.

12. the use of unproved accusations against political opponents

13. Many federal employees resigned or were dismissed.

14. It attacked and bullied them.

15. Americans were terrified of the Soviet Union and the threat of communism.

16. December 1954

RETEACHING ACTIVITY 27-1

Answers are listed from top of the chart to bottom.

Cause 1   Effects: 3, 5, 10, 12, 14

Cause 2   Effects: 2, 6, 7, 15

Cause 3   Effects: 1, 9, 11

Cause 4   Effects: 4, 8, 13

RETEACHING ACTIVITY 27-2

Postwar Economic Problems: 2, 7, 9, 13
Truman's Fair Deal: 1, 3, 5, 10, 12
Republican Proposals: 4, 6, 8, 11, 14

Essay

15. On Election Day experts still expected Dewey, who had a huge lead in the opinion polls, to win the election. Expectations were so great that the *Chicago Daily Tribune* wrongly published the headline that Dewey had defeated Truman. In fact, Truman had edged out Dewey in a narrow upset victory, winning by more than 2 million votes. Democrats also regained control of Congress.

16. Truman tried unsuccessfully to persuade Congress to pass legislation that would protect the voting rights of African Americans, abolish the poll tax, and make lynching a federal crime. He was successful in advancing civil rights by ordering federal departments and agencies to end job discrimination against African Americans and by ordering the armed forces to desegregate. He also instructed the Justice Department to actively enforce existing civil rights laws. In addition, Truman asked for the clearance of slums, government-backed medical insurance, higher minimum wages, and more federal money for public schools.

RETEACHING ACTIVITY 27-3

A. 5	**F.** 7	**K.** 6
B. 8	**G.** 13	**L.** 10
C. 3	**H.** 3	**M.** 2
D. 12	**I.** 7	**N.** 9
E. 1	**J.** 11	**O.** 4

Essay

As the stalemate between North Korea and South Korea dragged on, President Truman considered negotiating to end the war. General MacArthur wanted UN forces to attack China or bomb Chinese forces stationed in North Korea. MacArthur complained to Congress that the president would not let him do his job, saying in a letter that "There is no substitute for victory." Truman fired MacArthur, which caused a storm of protest in the United States. MacArthur was extremely popular and was given a hero's welcome when he returned to the country.

RETEACHING ACTIVITY 27-4

Red Scare: 8
HUAC: 2
McCarran Act: 9
Blacklist: 4
Julius & Ethel Rosenberg: 1
McCarthyism: 7
Hollywood Ten: 11
Whittaker Chambers: 3
Alger Hiss: 10

ANSWER KEY

Joseph McCarthy: 5
Loyalty Oath: 6

ENRICHMENT ACTIVITY 27-1

1. Vernon A. Walters
2. George H. W. Bush
3. George W. Ball and James R. Wiggins
4. two; Jeanne J. Kirkpatrick and Madeleine K. Albright
5. Henry Cabot Lodge, Jr.

Activity
Students' speeches will vary but should reflect an understanding of the United Nations' role in the world community.

ENRICHMENT ACTIVITY 27-2

1. 180
2. Franklin D. Roosevelt
3. 12 times
4. Andrew Johnson
5. The presidents of the 1900s used the power more frequently than the presidents of the 1800s.

Activity
Results of students' polls will vary with each individual. Combining the results of all students will result in a larger sample. This may be a good time to discuss things that might cause errors in sampling. For example, it is likely that many of the students will have asked the same people to respond to their poll, so their answers may be recorded twice. Results are also likely to be specific to a given region and may not reflect the whole country's viewpoint.

ENRICHMENT ACTIVITY 27-3

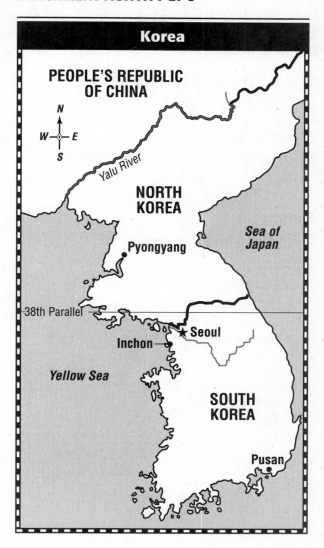

Students' maps should include the following labels in the correct location:

1. 38th parallel
2. North Korea, South Korea
3. Sea of Japan, Yellow Sea
4. Seoul
5. People's Republic of China, Yalu River
6. Pusan
7. Inchon
8. Pyongyang

ANSWER KEY

Activity

Students' travel scrapbooks will vary, but should show results of research. Accept all reasonable responses.

ENRICHMENT ACTIVITY 27-4

1. 1945
2. four years
3. Pilotless rocket missiles were built and the United States Navy tested the atomic bomb.
4. one year
5. The transistor was invented.

Activity

Students should note that most, if not all, of the inventions could be used for defense. Students should describe reasonable, defense-related uses. Students' memos will vary.

VOCABULARY ACTIVITY 28

1. per capita income
2. standard of living
3. moderate
4. surplus
5. affluence
6. domino theory
7. summit
8. productivity
9. automation
10. arms race
11. peaceful coexistence—In the 1950s this meant that the two superpowers (the United States and the Soviet Union) would compete with each other but would avoid war.

Using Vocabulary

Answers will vary but should reflect an understanding of the vocabulary words.

CHAPTER SKILLS ACTIVITY 28

1. United States total foreign aid, 1945–1961
2. 12%
3. 13 percent
4. foreign aid; The title states the topic presented in the graphic.

Activity

Summaries will vary depending on the song chosen, but should display understanding.

CRITICAL THINKING SKILLS ACTIVITY 28

Applying the Skill

1. F; This is a fact that can be verified by checking if armed conflicts occurred between the two nations.
2. F; Texts of speeches and newspapers of the day would show this was a fact.
3. O; Which nation was the "better" nation is a matter of opinion.
4. F; It is a matter of historical fact that the government of the United States feared the spread of communism and Soviet aggression during the 1950s.
5. F; The policy of massive retaliation is a matter of historical fact that can be verified.
6. F; The fact that the policy was called brinksmanship by critics can be verified.
7. O; Whether or not Eisenhower actually put the policy into effect can be verified, but whether he was tempted cannot be verified and would be opinion.
8. O; No one can know what would have happened, so this is opinion.

Practicing the Skill

1. C
2. A

GEOGRAPHY AND HISTORY ACTIVITY 28

1. The route of I-95 should be colored blue.

2. Interstate numbers I-84, I-80, and I-25 should be circled. The route using these highways should be traced in red.

3. Check students' maps to verify their routes.

4. Jacksonville, Florida, and Los Angeles, California, should be circled.

5. East-west roads have even numbers and are numbered from south to north. North-south roads have odd numbers and are numbered from west to east.

TIME LINE ACTIVITY 28

1. Lebanon

2. six days

3. 1979

4. Palestinian self-rule

5. Persian Gulf War

6. Suez-Sinai War

7. 1994

LINKING PAST AND PRESENT ACTIVITY 28

1. 1961; first human orbital flight

2. 1962; first American to orbit the earth

3. 1963; first woman in space

4. 1969; first moon landing

5. 1981; first reusable space vehicle

PRIMARY SOURCE READING ACTIVITY 28

Document-Based Question
Parents and police felt that rock 'n' roll contained suggestive and lewd words. A juke box trade journal stated that only low-minded listeners reading too much into the songs heard suggestive lyrics.

Students should locate articles or essays about music censorship. Their research should help them recognize that music preferred by young people is often different from the music of their parents, and that music thus becomes a symbol of the gap between the generations. In addition, students' responses should discuss whether music reflects the conditions in society (its violence, for example) or contributes to those conditions.

GUIDED READING ACTIVITY 28-1

1. Adlai E. Stevenson

2. John J. Sparkman

3. Dwight D. Eisenhower

4. Richard M. Nixon

5. supreme commander

6. Korea

7. Republican

8. moderate

9. private enterprise

10. December 1957

11. *Sputnik*

12. Cold War

13. Middle East

14. Budapest, Hungary

15. Soviet Union

16. NATO

17. "Spirit of Geneva"

18. peaceful coexistence

GUIDED READING ACTIVITY 28-2

1. the burst of military spending during the Korean War; government spending on housing, schools, welfare, highways, and veteran benefits; and technological advances

2. They weighed tons and filled whole rooms.

3. International Business Machines (IBM)

4. 46 percent, from $1,515 to $2,219

5. a growth in population, increased affluence, suburban expansion, and a greater demand for consumer goods

6. the baby boom

7. in the suburbs

8. William Levitt

9. Levittown

10. minorities, particularly African Americans and Hispanic Americans

11. the automobile

12. California

13. television, radio, and magazine advertising and marketing of products

14. television

15. rock 'n' roll

16. the generation gap

GUIDED READING ACTIVITY 28-3

1. business enterprises

2. urban areas

3. African American sharecroppers

4. synthetic fibers

5. coal industry

6. Appalachia

7. three million

8. Hispanics

9. ghettos

10. factories

11. John Kenneth Galbraith

12. the Beats

13. beatniks

14. Betty Friedan

15. suburban housewives

16. civil rights

RETEACHING ACTIVITY 28-1

I. **Education:** graduated from the United States Military Academy at West Point **Military Experience:** rose steadily through the army to become supreme commander of the Allied forces in Europe during World War II **Nickname:** Ike **Political Party:** Republican **Vice President:** Richard M. Nixon **Election Opponent:** Adlai E. Stevenson

II. Check marks should appear next to the following items: A, B, E, F, H

III. A. The Department of Health, Education, and Welfare 1. Oveta Culp Hobby **B. The Federal Highway Act 1.** to provide easy transportation for military forces in case of an attack **2.** the construction of more than 40,000 miles of highways that tied the nation together **C. New States 1.** Alaska and Hawaii joined the Union in 1959. **D. The Arms Race 1.** the United States and the Soviet Union

RETEACHING ACTIVITY 28-2

Contributors: C, F, K
Effects: Housing: D, M; Baby Boom: A, J; Car Culture: B, H; Consumerism: G, L; Entertainment: E, I

RETEACHING ACTIVITY 28-3

Across	Down
1. materialism	**1.** Montgomery
3. *The Affluent Society*	**2.** beatniks
4. *On the Road*	**5.** Appalachia
9. ghetto	**6.** Betty Friedan
10. white flight	**7.** Little Rock
11. automation	**8.** synthetics

ANSWER KEY

ENRICHMENT ACTIVITY 28-1

1. Tennessee
2. Hawaii
3. Arizona
4. Georgia
5. Alaska
6. Michigan
7. Louisiana
8. Pennsylvania
9. Indiana
10. Nevada

Activity

Brochures will vary but should accurately reflect the location students have chosen.

ENRICHMENT ACTIVITY 28-2

Color-coded dots should be placed reasonably accurately on students' maps to show a steady westward movement of the center of population.

ENRICHMENT ACTIVITY 28-3

Students' radio broadcasts should show a greater sensitivity and respect for migrant workers than the radio broadcast referred to in the song.

VOCABULARY ACTIVITY 29

1. segregation, integrate
2. civil disobedience, boycott, sit-in
3. Medicare, Medicaid
4. poverty line
5. interstate
6. Hispanic
7. feminist

CHAPTER SKILLS ACTIVITY 29

1. the struggle of Africans against colonial dominance
2. He believed that the colonial powers of Europe had created a negative image of Africans and that caused African Americans to think negatively about themselves.

3. He believed that the African American people in the United States should be concerned about the African struggle because their origins were in Africa.
4. Answers will vary, but students might say that a more positive image of Africa would increase self-esteem among African Americans and allow them to fight for their rights.

CRITICAL THINKING SKILLS ACTIVITY 29

Applying the Skill

1. The work harmed their education because they were often too tired to pay attention in class and often could not do homework because they had to work in the fields.
2. Students should conclude that Acuna does not think children should be migrant farmworkers. He paints a negative picture of the long hours that children had to work and the way their education suffered as a result. He says directly that "children are the ones hurt the most," in terms of not being able to stay in one school for any length of time or keep friends.
3. He thinks that higher wages would mean more stable families because workers would not have to work long hours in the fields. Families could also stay in one place instead of moving to find additional work. Students should conclude that higher salaries for adults might have also lowered the need for the labor of children.
4. No, Acuna does not think the general public knew about the working conditions of migrant workers. Students may conclude that Acuna thinks the public should have known about the hardships some families endured to put fruit and vegetables on people's tables. Students

may also conclude that Acuna thought the public might have done something to help the migrant workers had they known about working conditions.

Practicing the Skill

1. B
2. C
3. D

TIME LINE ACTIVITY 29

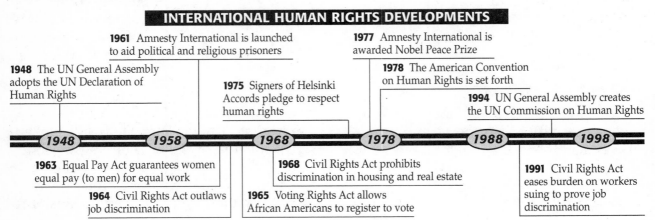

INTERNATIONAL HUMAN RIGHTS DEVELOPMENTS

1948 The UN General Assembly adopts the UN Declaration of Human Rights

1961 Amnesty International is launched to aid political and religious prisoners

1975 Signers of Helsinki Accords pledge to respect human rights

1977 Amnesty International is awarded Nobel Peace Prize

1978 The American Convention on Human Rights is set forth

1994 UN General Assembly creates the UN Commission on Human Rights

1948 *1958* *1968* *1978* *1988* *1998*

1963 Equal Pay Act guarantees women equal pay (to men) for equal work

1964 Civil Rights Act outlaws job discrimination

1968 Civil Rights Act prohibits discrimination in housing and real estate

1965 Voting Rights Act allows African Americans to register to vote

1991 Civil Rights Act eases burden on workers suing to prove job discrimination

LINKING PAST AND PRESENT ACTIVITY 29

Marches on Washington, D.C.

Event	Date	Number of Marchers
Vietnam War moratorium rally	November 15, 1969	600,000
Vietnam War "Out Now" rally	April 24, 1971	500,000
Return of hostages from Iran	January 27, 1981	500,000
20th anniversary of Civil Rights march	August 28, 1983	300,000
March for Women's Lives	April 5, 1992	750,000

GEOGRAPHY AND HISTORY ACTIVITY 29

1. Alabama should be colored red. The increase was 33.7 percent.
2. Louisiana should be colored blue. The increase was 11.9 percent.
3. Tennessee should be colored green.
4. Mississippi should be colored yellow.
5. Yes; the Voting Rights Act of 1965 achieved its objective because African American voter registration increased in every Southern state.

Answers will vary for the event facts, but students should be able to provide at least one detail about the march. Encourage students to share the event facts they found in a classroom discussion.

PRIMARY SOURCE READING ACTIVITY 29

1. Jobs now open only to white people will become available to African Americans.
2. Answers will vary but should include the basic information that a boycott is an economic form of protest. Boycotts are effective only when enough consumers band together to have an impact on the pocketbook of a business owner.

ANSWER KEY

Song lyrics will vary but should reflect a current civil rights issue.

GUIDED READING ACTIVITY 29-1

I. **A. 1.** NAACP (National Association for the Advancement of Colored People)

    2. Thurgood Marshall

  B. that it was unconstitutional to separate schoolchildren by race

  C. to make plans for integrating public schools

  D. 1. Governor Orval Faubus

    2. He sent federal troops to protect the African American students as they entered the school.

II. **A. 1.** Rosa Parks

    2. the Montgomery bus boycott

  B. 1. A. Philip Randolph

    2. Mohandas Gandhi

    3. Southern Christian Leadership Conference (SCLC)

GUIDED READING ACTIVITY 29-2

1. Kennedy was a Roman Catholic; voters were afraid he might show more loyalty to his church than to his country.

2. the story of how Kennedy rescued a crew member when the Japanese sank the PT boat he commanded

3. in 1946, when he won a seat in Congress from Massachusetts

4. the first televised presidential debate between the two candidates

5. New Frontier

6. increased government spending on social programs

7. a bill guaranteeing civil rights

8. On November 22, 1963 in Dallas, Texas

9. Lee Harvey Oswald; he was shot and killed by Jack Ruby two days after his arrest.

10. the Warren Commission

11. the "Great Society"

12. **a)** Head Start; **b)** Upward Bound; **c)** Job Corps; **d)** Volunteers in Service to America (VISTA)

13. Medicare and Medicaid

14. Department of Housing and Urban Development (HUD)

15. the Civil Rights Act of 1964

GUIDED READING ACTIVITY 29-3

1. Student Nonviolent Coordinating Committee (SNCC)

2. Freedom Riders

3. James Meredith

4. The governor of Mississippi aided by state police prevented Meredith from registering. Riots broke out; two people were killed, but Meredith registered.

5. He sent the Alabama National Guard to ensure the entry of African American students to the university.

6. on August 28, 1963 in Washington, D.C.

7. "We Shall Overcome"

8. "I have a dream. . ."

9. the Civil Rights Act of 1964

10. to help African Americans register to vote

11. the power to force local officials to allow African Americans to register to vote

12. Malcolm X

13. Stokely Carmichael

14. the Black Panthers

15. the Watts section of Los Angeles

16. On April 4, 1968 in Memphis, Tennessee

GUIDED READING ACTIVITY 29-4

1. feminists

2. National Organization for Women

3. Sandra Day O'Connor

4. Mexico

5. migrant farmworkers

6. César Chávez

7. United Farm Workers

8. New York City

9. Cuba

10. Fidel Castro

11. Indian Civil Rights Act of 1968

12. American Indian Movement

13. physical disabilities

RETEACHING ACTIVITY 29-1

Brown v. *Board of Education of Topeka, Kansas:* 3, 4, 5, 6, 12
Little Rock, Arkansas: 2, 7, 10, 11
Montgomery Bus Boycott: 1, 4, 8, 9
Martin Luther King, Jr.

1. Montgomery bus boycott

2. Gandhi had used nonviolent protest to help free the nation of India from Great Britain, using protest methods based on civil disobedience. King applied the same techniques to the struggle for African American rights in the United States.

3. Its leaders suggested nonviolent ways to react to taunts and jeers and showed civil rights workers how to protect themselves from violent attacks. The SCLC also discussed how to identify targets for protests and how to organize people for support.

RETEACHING ACTIVITY 29 -2

John F. Kennedy: A, B, E, F, H, I, M, O
Lyndon B. Johnson: D, G, J, L, N
Both: C, K

Essay

1. The debates were a turning point in the election. Until then Nixon had been leading in the polls. During the debate, Kennedy appeared handsome and youthful. Nixon, who was recovering from an illness, looked tired and sick. Kennedy spoke with confidence about the future. Many viewers thought that Kennedy made a better impression.

2. The Civil Rights Act of 1964 prohibited discrimination against African Americans in employment, voting, and public accommodations. It banned discrimination not only by race and color, but also by sex, religion, or national origin. The law passed because of President Johnson's legislative skill and Congress's desire to pay tribute to President Kennedy.

RETEACHING ACTIVITY 29-3

Ella Baker: 3
Malcolm X: 8
Robert Kennedy: 5
Freedom Riders: 9
James Meredith: 4
George Wallace: 1
Dr. Martin Luther King, Jr.: 7
Lyndon B. Johnson: 2
Black Panthers: 10
Stokely Carmichael: 6

RETEACHING ACTIVITY 29-4

Women: People: 3, 14; Organizations: 10; Laws: 15; Events: 18
Hispanic Americans: People: 2, 7, 12; Organizations: 11; Laws: 9; Events: 5, 17
Native Americans: People: 6, 16; Organizations: 1, 4; Laws: 13; Events: 8

Essay

One law concerned the removal of barriers that prevented some people from gaining access to public facilities. Another required employers to offer more opportunities for disabled people in the workplace. A third asserted the right of children with disabilities to equal educational opportunities.

ENRICHMENT ACTIVITY 29-1

1. 1896

2. *Sweatt* v. *Painter*

3. *Brown* v. *Board of Education of Topeka*

4. 8 years

5. *Plessy* v. *Ferguson*

Activity
Students' opinions will vary. Students should provide a sound argument to support the ruling. Students may mention that segregation was a legal responsibility of the schools not the parents, segregation would not work if it were left for parents to decide, parents' decisions might be unfair, and so on.

ENRICHMENT ACTIVITY 29-2

1. Speaker of the House

2. Secretary of Commerce

3. Secretary of Energy

4. Secretary of State

Activity
Students' plans will vary but should show an understanding of the importance of a quick takeover for national and interna-tional security. Students should present reasonable arguments for any changes they suggest in the order of succession and provide a long list to accommodate an unlikely situation in which many leaders die at once. Give students practice in nego-tiating a final list once they have presented convincing arguments.

ENRICHMENT ACTIVITY 29-3

Students may need to research to find the months of events not given in the text.

1. April 1963

2. May 1961

3. February 1960

4. June 1964

5. August 1965

6. August 1963

7. February 1965

8. June–August 1964

Activity
Students' time lines may vary but should include a minimum of the eight events listed above, correctly placed.

ENRICHMENT ACTIVITY 29-4

1. Wisconsin

2. in 1954; the act tried to use Menominee land for houses and to change their cul-tural identity

3. 5,000 years

4. a deep love and respect for the land and for all living things

Activity
Students' drawings will vary. The first drawing should show a peaceful scene of randomly placed log cabins, forests, a river, animals, and so on. The second drawing might show an urban or a suburban scene of many houses in the same area, with large farms, factories, and so on.

ANSWER KEY

VOCABULARY ACTIVITY 30

1. flexible response
2. executive order
3. exile
4. Vietcong
5. coup
6. escalate
7. search-and-destroy mission
8. counterculture
9. deferment
10. credibility gap
11. silent majority
12. MIAs

Using Vocabulary
Answers will vary but should reflect an understanding of the vocabulary words.

CHAPTER SKILLS ACTIVITY 30

Events chosen for inclusion may vary. Sample answers are given.

1965: Johnson begins to escalate United States involvement; Johnson; 180,000

1966: Fulbright hearings on war; Johnson; 390,000

1967: Stennis hearings on war; Johnson; 500,000

1968: Tet offensive; Johnson; 510,000

1969: Withdrawal of troops begins; Nixon; 485,000

1970: Invasion of Cambodia; Nixon; 334,000

1971: Invasion of Laos; Nixon; 60,000

1972: Heavy bombing of North Vietnam; Nixon; 10,000

1973: Peace agreement signed; Nixon; 5,000

Critical Thinking: It would be helpful to display records by troop strength to locate quickly the year of greatest or lowest troop strength or to see patterns in troop buildup.

CRITICAL THINKING SKILLS ACTIVITY 30

Applying the Skill

1. Students should infer that it was (at least in part) a response to the success of the Soviet Union placing a satellite in orbit.

2. The Soviet Union was more advanced because it put the first satellite into orbit, sent the first probe to the moon, and put the first astronaut into orbit before the United States sent its first astronaut into space.

3. Students should infer that establishing the ability to put astronauts into orbit and bring them safely back to Earth was a necessary step before deep space missions.

4. Students should infer that earlier missions to the moon gave scientists a lot of information, and that there is now a desire to discover new information about Mars, which could be a target for a future crewed space flight.

5. In the 1950s and early 1960s, the United States and the Soviet Union were the only nations involved in space exploration, and they launched only separate missions. From the mid-1980s onward, more nations became involved in space exploration, and joint projects involving more than one nation began.

Practicing the Skill

1. C
2. C
3. D

ANSWER KEY

GEOGRAPHY AND HISTORY ACTIVITY 30

1. Nixon—301 electoral votes
   Humphrey—191 electoral votes
   Wallace—46 electoral votes

2. the northeastern United States; Maine, New York, Massachusetts, Connecticut, Rhode Island, Pennsylvania, Maryland, and West Virginia should be colored red.

3. New York, Pennsylvania, and Texas should be outlined in black.

4. California should be colored blue.

5. Answers will vary but should note that the population of Texas is much larger than that of New Mexico (the number of a state's electoral votes is based on the number of congressional representatives, which is based on population size). Students may also note that New Mexico favored Nixon, and Texas favored Humphrey.

TIME LINE ACTIVITY 30

1. Fulgencio Batista
2. Dwight D. Eisenhower's
3. April 1961
4. October 1961
5. December 1961
6. Fidel Castro required $53 million worth of drugs and food from the United States.

LINKING PAST AND PRESENT ACTIVITY 30

Students' memorials will vary. They should honor a hero, such as a relative, historical figure, celebrity, or community leader. Students' memorials might take the form of drawings, clay models, or dioramas.

PRIMARY SOURCE READING ACTIVITY 30

Document-Based Question
Answers may include that Fred was not bitter or sad but that, like other soldiers, he paid the price for defending his country.

Answers will vary, but students' forewords should discuss the purposes of letters. These primary sources provide a sense of immediacy that can only be conveyed by people caught up in the events. Letters show varied viewpoints and attitudes. Letters from soldiers can be emotionally powerful, especially since the readers know whether the writer survived.

GUIDED READING ACTIVITY 30-1

I. A. 1. guerrilla warfare
     2. a military unit of the Special Forces who were trained to fight guerrilla wars

   B. 1. to counteract the appeal of communism in those places
     2. the Peace Corps
     3. to promote Latin America's growth

II. A. 1. April 17, 1961
      2. Within days Cuban forces crushed the invasion and captured the survivors.

   B. 1. to stop East Germans from fleeing to the West
     2. Communist repression

III. A. 1. The Soviets were building launching sites for nuclear missiles.
       2. to allow the superpower leaders to communicate instantly in times of crisis

III. B. 1. Soviet cosmonaut Yuri Gagarin
       2. Alan Shepard, Jr.; John Glenn
       3. July 20, 1969

ANSWER KEY

GUIDED READING ACTIVITY 30-2

1. Ho Chi Minh
2. French
3. Geneva Accords
4. Ngo Dinh Diem
5. National Liberation Front
6. Vietcong
7. November 1, 1963
8. coup
9. Gulf of Tonkin Resolution
10. 500,000
11. Operation Rolling Thunder
12. dense jungles
13. Ho Chi Minh Trail
14. search-and-destroy
15. Robert McNamara

GUIDED READING ACTIVITY 30-3

1. doves
2. hawks
3. More than 50,000 people marched to the Pentagon to protest the war.
4. Saigon and Hue
5. It developed a credibility gap.
6. Senator Eugene McCarthy of Minnesota, Senator Robert F. Kennedy of New York
7. that he would not seek another term as president
8. It triggered a rash of riots across the country; Americans, saddened by King's death, worried about the renewed urban violence.
9. Hubert H. Humphrey
10. Robert Kennedy won; later that night he was shot and killed.
11. Chicago

12. The protesters felt angry and excluded.
13. Chicago's mayor, Richard J. Daley, feared violence from the demonstrators.
14. It damaged Humphrey's candidacy; the Democrats appeared unable to control their convention.
15. Governor George C. Wallace of Alabama
16. the "silent majority" (or, the "quiet voice" of the "great majority of Americans, the nonshouters, the nondemonstrators")
17. It seemed that Americans wanted the government to restore order.

GUIDED READING ACTIVITY 30-4

1. draft deferments
2. birth date
3. Vietnamization
4. South Vietnam
5. Cambodia
6. antiwar protest
7. Henry Kissinger
8. antiwar movement
9. Cambodia
10. Kent State University
11. Jackson State
12. January 27, 1973
13. Saigon
14. April 30, 1975
15. 58,000
16. Vietnam Veterans Memorial

RETEACHING ACTIVITY 30-1

1. H, L
2. B, D
3. A, J
4. E, I
5. C, K
6. F, G

ANSWER KEY

RETEACHING ACTIVITY 30-2

A. 12	**G.** 5	**M.** 8
B. 3	**H.** 9	**N.** 5
C. 6	**I.** 13	**O.** 14
D. 11	**J.** 1	**P.** 2
E. 4	**K.** 7	**Q.** 10
F. 15	**L.** 16	

Essay

Dense jungles, muddy trails, and swampy rice paddies hampered troop movement. The South Vietnamese army did not always fight effectively. As the Vietcong guerrillas blended with the population, American soldiers found it hard to tell friends and enemies apart.

RETEACHING ACTIVITY 30-3

Across

5. deferments

8. radical

9. doves

Down

1. Robert F. Kennedy

2. convention

3. counterculture

4. draft

5. draft cards

6. Vietnam

7. hawks

RETEACHING ACTIVITY 30-4

Nixon's Peace with Honor Strategy
Draft Reform: 3, 4, 10, 14
Vietnamization: 11, 15
Intense Bombing: 1, 5
The Invasion of Cambodia
April 30, 1970: 8
May 4, 1970: 12
May 14, 1970: 7
The War Ends
Fall 1972: 16
December 1972: 2
January 27, 1973: 9
Early 1975: 13
April 30, 1975: 6

ENRICHMENT ACTIVITY 30-1

1. Students can name any four of the following countries: Belize, Guatemala, El Salvador, Honduras, Nicaragua, Costa Rica, Panama.

2. 10 countries

3. about 75 percent (77 percent)

4. Suriname, French Guiana, Argentina; Students may need to use another map to find the names of these countries.

Activity

Students' scrapbooks and presentations will vary. Students should include details that show geographic knowledge of the country they selected, an understanding of the kinds of things Peace Corps workers helped with, and basic knowledge of the culture, language, and time period.

ENRICHMENT ACTIVITY 30-2

Students' maps should include the following labels in the correct location:

1. North Vietnam, South Vietnam

2. Gulf of Tonkin, South China Sea

3. Ho Chi Minh Trail, Laos

4. Da Nang

5. Saigon

6. Hanoi

7. Mekong River, Thailand, Cambodia, Mekong Delta

ENRICHMENT ACTIVITY 30-3

1. the first piloted flight of the command-service module

2. *Apollo-Saturn 8*

3. 3

4. first stage—kerosene and liquid oxygen

second stage—liquid hydrogen and liquid oxygen

third stage—liquid hydrogen and liquid oxygen

Activity

Students should accurately reproduce the diagram of the Saturn-Apollo rocket as the central focus of their collages. The collages will vary.

ENRICHMENT ACTIVITY 30-4

1. army

2. about 5,500

3. about 1,500

4. about 53 percent

Activity

Students should understand from the activity that drawing conclusions about the percentage of MIAs and prisoners from each branch can only be done if they know how many served in each branch.

ANSWER KEY

ANSWER KEY

ANSWER KEY